Here Comes Tomorrow!

HERE COMES TOMORROW!

Living and Working
in the Year 2000

———◆—◆———

By the Staff of
THE WALL STREET JOURNAL

DOW JONES BOOKS
Princeton, New Jersey

Preface

How will we meet our soaring needs for living space, for food and for energy to drive our automated factories in the decades just before us? What will our homes be like and will the new leisure given us by electronic housekeeping devices be used for good or ill? Will our cities be fit to live in or blighted by polluted air and water? Will we live longer? What will our lives be like?

These are some of the intriguing questions explored in detail by *Here Comes Tomorrow!* Originally printed as a series of articles in The Wall Street Journal, these chapters attracted wide attention at the time. They now are being published in more permanent form for the benefit of students, planners, corporate managers and others concerned with the not-so-distant future.

Although these chapters deal with a host of subjects, the future is a big place and a lot of things are going to happen there. The past can remind us of the dangers in attempting to predict the future, in all its diversity and uncertainty.

In 1878 a young American inventor named Thomas

A. Edison was trying to develop an electric light. As Arthur C. Clarke, the scientist-author, tells the story, the British Parliament set up a committee to determine if the undertaking held any promise. The committee's conclusion, based on the testimony of experts, was that Edison's ideas on electric illumination were "unworthy of the attention of practical or scientific men."

That blunder serves as sufficient warning to anyone who sets out to discern the future. The record of the past is filled with examples of learned men who proved conclusively that airplanes could never fly or that the very idea of intercontinental ballistic missiles was absurd. History also offers examples of developments that caught most men completely unaware—such as the atomic bomb.

Despite the pitfalls, the future remains an irresistibly tempting subject for speculation. For one reason, it's fascinating to ponder life decades or centuries from now; witness the enduring popularity of science fiction.

For another, thinking about the future can be useful. If we can see the directions in which science, population changes, economics and other forces are taking us, we at least have a chance to try to steer clear of dangers. If we see, for example, that population growth threatens to outstrip food supplies in some areas, the knowledge will help to focus the efforts of governments and scientists on the task of increasing food production. If we see that our cities are growing formlessly and eating up vital recreational areas, we can take a closer look at the ways we are using land in urban areas. Or if we grasp the immense capabilities of the computer for cataloging information about all of us, we can make rules that prevent such use of computers from destroying our privacy.

It was both for sheer interest's sake and in the hope of shedding useful light on things to come that The Wall Street Journal set out to do a series of articles on the future. By the standards of science fiction writers, who often roam centuries ahead, the time span covered is modest—between now and the year 2000. But though bizarre speculations about the distant future are missing, much that is exciting remains. Sticking to the next few decades also makes firmer forecasts possible, since much of the research basic to the technological developments expected before the end of this century is already well along. The materials that will be used in the engines of 4,000-mile-an-hour commercial airliners are being tested in laboratories today, and the theoretical work has been done for such wonders as computerized credit systems and three-dimensional television.

The series was planned by Sterling E. Soderlind, an assistant managing editor of The Wall Street Journal. Of necessity, all the articles but one were written on the premise that the world would not be engulfed in a nuclear holocaust; the one exception is the article on military developments, which examines planning for possible nuclear conflicts.

The individual chapters are the work of 13 reporters on the staff of The Wall Street Journal. To gather information, they talked with scores of scientists and authorities in various fields. Often it was possible for them to examine parts of the future already taking shape—from the New Towns going up near Washington, D.C., to mock-ups of the cabins of tomorrow's airliners.

Their reports represent a serious attempt to define the most likely possibilities for various aspects of our future. The dominant theme is that the future holds a mixture of promise and peril. And the hope of the editors and authors is that the more we know about the possibilities, the better our chances for avoiding the peril and realizing the promise.

PAUL LANCASTER
Editor

Contents

Population:

Easing the Crush

In the year 2000 there will be more than six billion people in the world, double the present total. The population of the United States will be close to 340 million, compared with 198 million now.

The prospect seems horrifying. For impoverished lands whose food supplies already are stretched thin, it raises the specter of worsening hunger. For American city dwellers whose nerves already are rubbed raw by the crowds and clangor of urban life, it evokes nightmares of people trampling one another underfoot.

But will it really be all that bad?

Probably not. Population growth obviously does pose serious challenges to government and private planners, and it inevitably will change life in some unwelcome ways. But major efforts are under way to cope with the problems arising from increased numbers of people.

Agricultural scientists, food technologists and fisheries experts have come up with a variety of proposals for increasing the world's food supply. In the United States, Federal officials have mapped a vast expansion

1

of the national parks to accommodate additional citizens. City planners are devising new housing schemes that will leave large open spaces, as well as new types of transit that will speed travel in sprawling metropolitan areas. In some of the overseas areas where the squeeze between population and food is most severe, birth control is winning acceptance.

Population trends clearly are a major factor in all planning for the future, and they are the subject of constant study. Particularly intense research has been done on United States population growth and the changes that will accompany it in various areas of American life.

The Census Bureau has made four different projections of United States population growth over the next few decades. Each projection is based on a different assumption about American birth-rate trends, but all reflect the Census Bureau's belief that by the end of the century American life expectancy at birth will average 72 years, only two years more than at present.

So far it appears that the next-to-highest of the projections is the most accurate. This projection puts United States population in 1985 at 262,926,000 and in 2000 at 338,219,000. The precise figure for United States population, shown on the Commerce Department's population "clock" at 8:00 a.m. Jan. 1, 1967, was 197,926,341.

The Census Bureau expects some changes in the makeup of the American population by 2000, but these do not appear particularly startling. The broad break-down by age will show little change from the present pattern—40% under 20, 51% in the 20-to-64 bracket and 9% over 64. The Bureau sees the nonwhite portion of the United States population increasing from the present 12% to about 14% by the end of the century.

The doubling of world population over the next generation—a projection made by the United Nations and a number of other organizations—also is sure to have immense impact on America.

Population growth abroad could prove a bonanza for United States businesses that sell their wares and services around the globe, particularly if modern technology can raise living standards faster than human beings multiply. Some economists note that, by chance or not, big population gains generally have coincided with prosperous times. But if population growth means that life in the world's "have-not" nations becomes even grimmer, the resulting discontent and territorial pressures could add to international turmoil and unrest—and to Washington's headaches.

Analysts agree that birth-control programs hold the key to whether population increases will outstrip food supplies in underdeveloped nations. Right now most poor nations are adding people faster than they are expanding food production. Many rely heavily on United States food shipments.

A report by the Population Council, a nonprofit or-

3

ganization that studies world population developments, provides at least some grounds for optimism on efforts to curb runaway population growth. It indicates that birth-control programs are making headway in some of the lands where population problems are most acute.

India is an example. It now has a population of about 490 million, more than the entire Western Hemisphere. An Indian official recently estimated that if present population trends continue and birth-control efforts fail, the nation's population would exceed one billion by the year 2000.

Since 1951, however, family planning has been a national policy in India. Lately the government has been spending some $15 million annually on birth control, and in 1966 the outlay rose to $40 million. The goal is to reduce the annual rate from the current level of 40 births per 1,000 persons to 25 by 1971 (the present rate in the United States is 19 per 1,000).

In 1965 the Indian government approved use of the new intrauterine contraceptive device (IUD), generally considered to be the cheapest effective birth-control method. Since mid-1965 about one million IUDs have been inserted under the government program. In addition, since 1963 the government has paid for one million voluntary male sterilizations. The Population Council comments that birth control "now seems to be gaining some momentum" in India.

Red China, with some 700 million citizens, is also

4

promoting family planning; birth-control devices and information are supplied as part of the government's public health program. Other low-income Asian nations where birth-control drives are under way include Pakistan, South Korea, Taiwan and Malaysia. In Africa the United Arab Republic, Tunisia and Kenya are pressing birth-control programs.

Birth-control efforts have generally lagged in Latin America. This area, with a total population of about 250 million, has the highest rate of population growth in the world, about 2.8% a year (the world average is about 2%). According to the Population Council, Latin America has resisted birth control "in part because of the predominantly Catholic religion and in part because of the countries' traditional image of themselves as underpopulated, with large areas capable of new settlement."

There are signs this situation may be changing, however. Government-supported family-planning campaigns have been launched in Chile, Honduras, Venezuela, Peru and Jamaica. In Colombia a nongovernmental birth-control drive has started.

Even with birth control, the earth—including the United States—is going to get more crowded. And even though population growth is not expected to lead to mass starvation or the other catastrophes sometimes envisioned, the projected increases are large enough to give rise to serious questions about what life will be like a generation from now.

Besides the concern about whether men will have enough elbow room or whether golf courses and parks will be hopelessly jammed, there are questions such as these: What will happen to privacy? Will man be able to escape noise? Will the psychological pressures of crowding damage man's health? Will man's environment be polluted beyond repair?

Definitive answers aren't possible. A great deal depends on how much serious thinking about the future is done in and out of government here and abroad in the years immediately ahead. Fortunately, much scholarly attention is now being focused on the problems of the future.

Consider the matter of recreational space in the United States. In the year 2000 population will probably be about 70% above today's total, but no more land will be available. Many analysts believe—the difficulties of urban life notwithstanding—that Americans will continue to move from rural areas to cities in the years ahead. By one estimate, five of every six Americans will live in urban areas in 2000, compared with roughly four in six now.

According to this projection, population density in the urban United States will reach about 4,000 persons per square mile by the year 2000, up from about 3,000 per square mile at present. At the same time, the population pattern in the rural areas of the central part of the country is not expected to change significantly.

This region, embracing the plains and mountain states, has actually been losing population during the past two decades and is expected to remain relatively sparsely settled.

Roger Revelle, director of Harvard University's Center for Population Studies, estimates that in 2000 there will be two Americans for every foot of coastline in the country. If present practices continue, only a fraction of this will be available for public recreation. Mr. Revelle's recommendation: Build artificial offshore islands for Twenty-first Century ocean bathers.

Mr. Revelle also foresees a shortage of inland park facilities. With more people and with automation giving them more leisure, the number of visits to municipal playgrounds, parks, zoos and golf courses may rise as much as 400% by 2000, according to Mr. Revelle.

To accommodate this increase, he says, not only must more land be set aside for parks and similar facilities but "we need to find new patterns of use that will allow the number of visitors to be greatly increased." Among the possibilities suggested by Mr. Revelle—some of which admittedly might detract a bit from the charms of the wilderness—are wear-resistant footpaths through forests; electronic guide systems and fences that would keep crowds of hikers from tripping over each other; staggered visiting hours; and a rationing system that would allot each family a certain number of park visits per year.

7

How society copes with some of the problems stemming from population increases will depend heavily on evolving attitudes of courts and legislatures. Noise and sign-cluttered landscapes seem certain to aggravate people more as crowding increases, and they may demand new legal controls to keep life bearable.

Physical as well as mental health could be affected by crowding, according to experts. Studies already have suggested a link between heart trouble and overcrowding. And there is a well-established connection between air pollution—which seems certain to become more of a problem as the number of people rises—and respiratory troubles.

Harvey S. Perloff, who directs regional and urban studies for a nonprofit research organization called Resources for the Future, warns: "Unless some startling and currently unforeseen technological advances come along, it well may be that by the turn of the century pure air, far from being free, could require a greater public and private annual outlay than any other single resource category. It could become the 'scarcest' natural resource, in the sense of experiencing the most sharply increasing costs."

Despite the possibility that reducing air pollution will impose burdensome costs, most analysts take a rosy view of the economic changes that are expected to accompany population growth in the United States.

Probing deeply into the anticipated age breakdown

8

of the United States population in 2000, they say the absence of important changes in the proportion of young or old people should not obscure the prospect of at least one economically significant development. This is the expectation that within the 20-to-64 group the number of 20-to-44-year-olds will increase from 31% of the total United States population to 35%. The projected level is regarded by economists as more normal than the present one, which reflects unusually low birth rates during the depression of the 1930s and during World War II.

The meaning of this age shift for the economy is clear. The 20-to-44-year-olds are the group that forms families, needs new homes, new cars and new appliances—and thus consumes the most. Its above-average expansion in coming years, most forecasters are convinced, constitutes a solid plus for tomorrow's economy.

This bulge in the ranks of big spenders will combine with the growth of the total population and with productivity increases to send the United States gross national product soaring. A study made for a Government agency by the Washington-based National Planning Association (NPA) sees the GNP exceeding $2 trillion by 2000. The following table, taken from the NPA report, traces this anticipated rise. The figures represent billions of dollars, expressed in terms of 1960 prices.

		GNP
1965	....	$ 629
1970	....	748
1980	....	1,110
1990	....	1,600
2000	....	2,280

Resources for the Future offers some educated guesses about the makeup of the $2 trillion-plus GNP it too envisions for the year 2000. It figures government expenditures will account for 25% of the total GNP, up from 20% at present; the change will reflect the increased demand for government services such as police and fire protection, sanitation and recreation that will accompany urbanization. Consumer spending will drop to 60% of the total GNP from 65% now. The third major component of the GNP, investment spending by business, is expected to account for some 15% of the total, about the same portion as currently.

The most striking feature of the GNP forecasts is that they show the nation's output of goods and services rising almost four times faster than the United States population. If they are correct, Americans living in the year 2000 will have an even greater abundance of comforts and conveniences than they now possess.

Personal income also is expected to increase far faster than the population. In terms of 1960 prices, the United States income total in 2000 will exceed $1.7 trillion, up from $530 billion last year, according to the NPA. Resources for the Future sees changes in the way consumers will spend their rising incomes in coming decades; a smaller portion of their budgets will go for such items as food, clothing, alcohol and tobacco, while more will be spent on education, recreation, household appliances and furniture.

A substantial part of the increase in the national wealth will result from improvement in the productivity of the labor force. Helped by more efficient machines and work methods, the average employe in 2000 in one hour will turn out $10.50 worth of goods and services in terms of 1960 prices, the NPA estimates. The comparable figure for 1965 was $4.18.

Allowing both for productivity gains and a rise in the United States work force, Resources for the Future forecasts that the nation's factories will turn out nearly four times their present volume of goods in 2000. New housing starts will total 4.2 million units in 2000, roughly three times recent annual rates.

The highly productive employe of 2000 will work a week that his 1966 counterpart would envy, NPA believes. It will be only 31 hours long, on the average, barely three-quarters the length of today's average workweek.

The labor force of the year 2000 will be deployed very differently from today, NPA estimates. The follow-

11

ing table, taken from the study, shows the percentage of United States workers in various occupations, now and in 2000.

	Now	In 2000
Manufacturing	25%	18%
Trade	19%	17%
Misc. Services	18%	28%
Government	13%	17%
Construction	6%	7%
Utilities	6%	3%
Agriculture	6%	2%
Finance	5%	6%
Other	2%	2%

The number of persons in the "miscellaneous services" group will pass the "manufacturing" total in the early 1980s according to the study. And by 2000 nearly as many persons will be working in "government" occupations as for manufacturing companies.

—ALFRED L. MALABRE, JR.

Food:

Where It Will Come From

In the year 2000 the United States farmer will be a sophisticated executive with a computer for a foreman. The fisherman will be a farmer methodically harvesting the oceans. The rancher will ride herd on nothing more ornery than huge livestock hotels where every aspect of the environment is precisely controlled.

As a result, Americans will eat better than ever, despite a population far larger than today's. Food pills, though they are under development at Pillsbury Company and elsewhere for possible use in the space program, will remain the gourmet's nightmare of a more distant future. At the very worst, a budget-minded housewife might serve up tasty dishes that look like meat but have really been created from the protein of soybeans or algae—at half the cost and twice the convenience of the real thing.

In general, say agricultural scientists and food technologists, the outlook in the United States is for more of the same foods we eat today, only better and quite possibly cheaper. Accompanying these improvements, add

13

the experts, will be technological progress that will largely eliminate differences between the production of food and the production of manufactured goods such as cars.

The impact of labor-saving equipment on farming is already clear. In 1880 it took a United States farmer 46 man-hours to plant, cultivate and harvest an acre of corn. In 1960 it took seven hours, and by 1965 progressive farmers were doing the job in two hours.

Likewise, the impact of technological and management advances on yields is dramatic. The farmer of 1950 harvested an average of 38 bushels of corn per acre. By 1965 corn yields had nearly doubled—and nearly 10% of American farmers were achieving yields of 150 bushels an acre.

In the not-too-distant future highly automated systems may help make it possible to produce close to 500 bushels of corn an acre—in even less than the two hours it now takes the most efficient farmers to work an acre. A distinguishing feature of rural America in the year 2000 suggests L. S. Fife, agricultural economist for International Harvester Company, will be towers containing television scanners to keep an eye on robot tractors.

Adds Anthony E. Cascino, a vice president of International Minerals and Chemical Company, which is a major fertilizer producer: "The owner of the farm of the future will no more be out riding a tractor than the president of General Motors is out on an assembly line tightening bolts."

For most of the rest of the world, however, the food outlook isn't so bright. It's estimated 300 million to 500 million persons currently live on the brink of starvation in Asia, Africa, Latin America and the Mideast. Another 1.5 billion of the world's total population of more than 3 billion people are malnourished, prey to disease and often too listless to struggle effectively against their poverty.

Distressing as this picture is, the future could be darker unless great strides are made in food production. By the end of this century, the population of the under-developed regions of the globe is expected to more than double to about 5 billion. To feed these masses and improve their diet modestly over the present unsatisfactory standards, food supplies would have to increase 306% in the Far East, 207% in the Mideast, 238% in Latin America and 159% in Africa, according to the United Nations. By contrast, food production in these areas as a whole rose 54% during the past 25 years.

Even more alarming, per-capita food production in these regions has actually been declining between 1% and 2% a year since the 1958–60 period. United States food shipments have filled the gap in many countries, but American surpluses no longer exist in substantial quantities. By 1985, Secretary of Agriculture Orville R. Freeman warns, the annual food deficit in the under-

15

developed countries may widen to the equivalent of 88 million tons of food grain—more than three times the weight of annual food shipments from the developed to the underdeveloped lands in the 1960s.

Most observers refuse to forecast a truly catastrophic famine in underdeveloped areas of the world between now and the end of the century, but the squeeze between population and food production nevertheless has chilling implications. Arthur D. Odell, manager of a General Mills Incorporated project to develop futuristic foods from isolated protein, talks of a "biological rebalance"—a thinning out of the world's population that might result from wars fanned by food shortages.

Indeed, food already is a major force in world power politics. Specialists on Russia speculate that the Soviet's huge purchases of Canadian wheat in 1966 were made to block Red China from outside sources of supply. Assessing the current conflict in Southeast Asia, Mr. Odell says that "the Communists don't want South Vietnam—they want the Mekong Delta." The Delta is a rich rice-growing area in South Vietnam.

The world food situation is of immense significance to United States taxpayers. In addition to shipments of food abroad by the United States Government, which are expected to rise from the present annual rate of $1.6 billion to a level of $2 billion to $3 billion in coming years, Roger Revelle, director of Harvard University's Center for Population Studies, estimates that agricul-

16

tural capital investments totaling at least $80 billion will be needed over the next 14 years if the underdeveloped nations are to reach minimum self-sufficiency. On the basis of Washington's past role in agricultural investment overseas, the United States share of this outlay would amount to about $1.5 billion annually, he says.

"This violates the cherished tenets of the American Government and people that somehow the foreign aid business is going to come to an end very soon," observes Mr. Revelle.

The pressure of food shortages abroad, coupled with the anticipated jump in the United States population from 198 million now to almost 340 million by 2000, is expected to provide the impetus for great strides ahead in the science of farming, just as the exigencies of war force breakthroughs in the science of weaponry. Already, according to Wendell Clithero, an agricultural specialist with International Business Machines Corporation, there are no less than 48,000 agricultural research projects under way in the United States. For a glimpse of the future, consider a few of them:

Using wide-spectrum fluorescent lights, Sylvania Electric Products Incorporated has found it can speed the growth of some plants 25% to 30%. Tomatoes, for instance, might be grown faster and in larger quantities on huge indoor "farms" using artificial light. By the same token, in times of oversupply and low prices, plant

17

growth could be arrested for weeks or months without damaging quality.

Oil companies have found that 1,000 pounds of bacteria and certain yeasts, placed in a fermentation tank with water, crude oil stock, nitrogen and phosphate compounds, will multiply to 5,000 pounds in 24 hours, ultimately producing a bland powder of 60% high-quality protein and vitamin content. Scientists are trying to convert the powder into products that taste like meat or fish.

National Science Foundation weather modification experts suggest sending supersonic aircraft aloft over areas threatened by hail. Laboratory experiments indicate shock waves projected into the clouds by sonic booms might prevent ice crystals from enlarging into crop-damaging hailstones.

In one way or another, most experimental work is directed at increasing the efficiency with which man can produce food on the 3½ billion acres of the Earth's surface already under cultivation. Additional potential arable land is estimated at about 2½ billion acres, but most of this is tropical rain forest with poor soil, savannah land alternating between drought and flood, or desert.

To be sure, future developments probably will result in some of this marginal land coming under cultivation. Desalination of the seas and brackish lakes for irrigation water is a distinct possibility by the end of the century, and Government scientists have concluded it's possible to increase rainfall by seeding clouds with silver iodide particles.

Another possibility is to develop crops that can survive in hostile environments. Sanford Siegel, a botanist working at Union Carbide Corporation's Tarrytown, New York, research institute, has discovered that rice will produce normal yields in saline water if extra oxygen is pumped in. He envisions aerated brine ponds along the Asian coast in which millions of bushels of rice could be grown.

But a sobering example of what is involved in opening up new land for cultivation is furnished by the experience of the United Arab Republic. The Aswan Dam, spanning the Nile, will increase Egypt's cropland by a spectacular 30%—but at a cost of $1 billion and 15 years of research, engineering and construction. By the time the dam is completed, probably in 1968, Egypt's population will be 35% greater than at the start of the project.

"To increase the world's cropland availability in the same proportion, that is, about 30%, would cost on the same basis about $450 billion," says John J. Haggerty, vice president and research director of Agri Research Incorporated, Manhattan, Kansas.

At any rate, argues International Minerals and Chemical, "under the most optimistic assumptions, approximately two-thirds of the vital future food production

19

increases will have to come from improved yields on land already under cultivation."

That advanced technology can increase yields dramatically has been amply demonstrated. With the aid of Rockefeller Foundation scientists, Mexico in the past 15 years has transformed itself from a net importer of foodstuffs to a net exporter. This has come about through the education of farmers in fertilization and irrigation and through the painstaking development of hybrid seeds adapted to local soils and climates. Output of potatoes in Mexico has tripled, bean and wheat crops have quadrupled and corn production has tripled.

Technology now under development may permit underdeveloped countries to leapfrog ahead even faster. International Minerals and Chemical is working on a growth regulator, triiodobenzoic acid (tiba), one ounce of which may increase soybean yields 10% to 15% by changing the shape of the plant and reducing the amount of leaves and stems that compete with beans for soil nutrients. In 1966, University of California scientists announced they had duplicated photosynthesis outside a living cell for the first time. It's hoped that eventually photosynthesis—the process by which sunlight is converted to proteins, fats, sugars and starches—can be manipulated to produce nutritious food from almost any form of plant life.

Pesticide research is another avenue to improved yields. Insects still reduce agricultural productivity in the United States by as much as 30% on some crops, and losses are even higher abroad. An ironic effect of an increase in yields is that it creates a dangerously healthy environment for destructive insects.

Some experts suggest that an alternative to the complex task of applying chemicals to crops is the use of "biological" pesticides. These can be insects or viruses that feed on pests. They also can consist of sterilized males of the pest species; by competing with fertile males, they impede reproduction. Another suggestion comes from IBM. It proposes using a satellite that could predict crop infestations by using already available sensing devices to follow bug migrations; knowing where insects were set to strike, farmers could use chemical or biological pesticides in a limited, highly selective fashion.

But pesticides, fertilizers and water are only part of the solution to the world's food problem, authorities stress. As Purdue University economist N. S. Hadley puts it, "the real race is between population and education."

India's 60 million farmers speak dozens of different dialects. Most are illiterate. "How effective would the agricultural extension service of the United States be under similar circumstances?" asks Mr. Hadley. Over the past 25 years yields per acre have increased 109% in North America; in the less developed regions yields have risen only 8%.

It's estimated that half of all Indians subsist on less than 1,600 calories daily. This compares with an average of about 3,100 in the United States.

An even more serious problem in India and other poor countries is a lack of protein. Proteins—the body's "building blocks"—are essential to normal cellular growth. The grains and vegetables that comprise most of the diet in underdeveloped lands are deficient in high-quality protein; in particular, they are low in some of the proteins containing amino acids, substances that are vital for healthy development and that Americans get in quantity from animal or fish products. In babies raised without sufficient protein—those raised on a diet of corn, for example—the growth of brain cells and bone structure is often retarded.

Underdeveloped countries need their grain to meet immediate food needs and thus can't convert it into high-quality protein such as beef or pork. But a source of high-quality exists in great abundance in the oceans in the form of fish and other marine life.

Currently, fin-fish (as opposed to shellfish) production amounts to only about 60 million tons annually. It's estimated that this could be quadrupled without depleting the oceans; moreover, fish protein would cost only about 20 cents a pound, compared with more than $2 for an equivalent amount of protein from hamburger.

Victor L. Loosanoff, former senior scientist with the United States Bureau of Commercial Fisheries, suggests that the world of the year 2000 will have added a new word to its lexicon—"mariculture." The first step, he says, would be to cultivate seaweeds rich in protein, such as chlorella, which has a flavor like lima beans and is sometimes used now as a food ingredient in Japan. Another undertaking might be the production of ocean algae, also a good protein source, in shallow basins, using fertilizers and pesticides to maximize yields.

The next step, theorizes Mr. Loosanoff, would be to gain an understanding of the environmental habits of shellfish and crustaceans. An experiment in Italy has demonstrated that one acre of the bottom of a screened-off estuary can yield 100,000 pounds of shellfish a year. A South Carolina scientist has shown that shrimp can be grown in large quantities in specially constructed ponds costing only $35 to $50 an acre to build; a substantial shrimp-raising facility of this type could be built at a fraction of the cost of a modern shrimp trawler.

Farming of fin-fish also offers tantalizing possibilities. Lauren Donaldson, a University of Washington fisheries expert and geneticist, has achieved spectacular results in work on hybrid salmon and trout. Over a period of 30 years, Mr. Donaldson has developed a select strain of rainbow trout that weigh up to three pounds when a year old—250 times the ordinary weight of a yearling rainbow. At three years, the fish weigh as much as 17½ pounds. Mr. Donaldson is attempting to crossbreed his

23

giants with steelhead trout; like salmon, the steelhead migrate to sea and return with unerring instinct to their birthplace when it comes time to mate.

In the future, fish "ranches" might dot the seacoasts of the world. Improved salmon and trout could be raised to migratory size, then released to "pasture" in the open sea until sexual instinct drove them home for "roundup." To simplify marketing, the fish could be irradiated to kill spoiling microbes or perhaps sprayed with a chemical coating that would both retard spoilage from the air and serve as an edible package.

Protein deficiency also may be alleviated by two other research developments. One is the work of a group of Purdue geneticists and biochemists. They have achieved a breakthrough by altering the genetic composition of corn so that lysine, one of the essential amino acids, is present in increased quantities, giving the corn a nutritional value similar to milk. Rats fed on "Opaque 2" corn, as it's called, gained weight more than three times as fast as those fed on ordinary hybrid corn; pigs started on Opaque 2 at 130 pounds gained weight 50% faster than other pigs.

By 1975, says Oliver E. Nelson, one of the Purdue scientists, Opaque 2 could be incorporated into high-yielding hybrid corns indigenous to various parts of the world. The implications for people like the Guatemalans, who obtain 70% of their protein from such corn-based foods as tortillas, are enormous. It's thought that eventually the protein content and quality of wheat and rice might also be improved, despite their more complicated genetic composition.

A second laboratory breakthrough that holds promise for increasing the supply of protein is the development of the capability to shape pure protein into palatable foods. General Mills has come up with a process for refining the protein out of soybeans, spinning it into fiber and, through the use of flavoring and binding agents such as egg albumin, reconstituting the fiber in high-protein chunks of food that are difficult to distinguish from real meat.

Such synthetic entrees, known as "analogs," have a versatility that is "staggering," according to Arthur Odell of General Mills. "Analogs can be produced to meet almost any conceivable dietary, religious, ethnic or geographic ground rules."

More important, the analogs can be produced with an efficiency of 80%—in other words, only 20% of the protein is lost in converting soybeans to analogs. This is 10 times more efficient than a steer's conversion of grain into protein. And, on average, the analog costs only half as much as meat with comparable protein.

Most experts agree, however, that there will be room for both meat and analogs in the years ahead. John Murphy, research director for Swift and Company, foresees analogs being used in stews, chili, casseroles and processed "meats," while more real meat will be available for roasts and steaks. "But frankly," says Mr. Murphy, "I think the analog people will find it smarter not to compete directly with meat—they could come up with food ideas we haven't even thought about."

While efforts to ease hunger abroad may stimulate changes in domestic foods, the main thrust of United States agriculture will continue to be to increase efficiency in the production of present foods. The biggest single advance is expected to be the use of computers in agriculture, a practice researchers say will be widespread by 1975.

Already some 10,000 to 15,000 farmers are using computer-equipped data-processing centers to help them with bookkeeping. But in the years ahead farmers are expected to rely on computers for aid in planning their operations.

Farming has become a highly complex business, with the level of profit governed by how well a farmer chooses among variables such as types of crops and seed and quantity and type of fertilizer. Computers could prove invaluable in guiding farmers to the best decisions, agricultural experts contend. They cite the following example of a Prairie City, Illinois, farmer who last year competed against an International Minerals and Chemical computer to see whether man or machine could come up with the most profitable plan for a farm:

With both the computer and the farmer using the same anticipated operating costs and market prices, the farmer chose to plant 98 acres in corn, 16 acres in oats, 20 acres in alfalfa, 20 acres in soybeans and 8 acres in wheat. Based on this planting scheme and his choice of fertilizers, the farmer arrived at an estimated gross profit of $6,789.

The computer told the farmer he was all wet. It calculated that by planting 134 acres in corn, 20 acres in alfalfa and 8 acres in wheat and by using different intensities of fertilizer, profit would zoom to $8,829, an increase of 30%.

It's true that computers are a bit steep to lease or own on a gross income of $8,829. But farms are rapidly becoming both fewer and bigger. There are now 3.2 million farms in the United States, 42% less than in 1950, and it's estimated that 140,000 of these produce 42% of the nation's foodstuffs. By 1975, the Agriculture Department estimates, there will be only 2 million farms.

Victor Chou, agricultural economist for Allis-Chalmers Corporation, predicts that by 1975 the "average level of investment per farm will skyrocket from the present $100,000 to $250,000." Remarks another farm economist: "With an investment of that size, a computer isn't just a cute gimmick; it's a necessity if you aren't going to lose your shirt." Except on the largest spreads, however, it's likely that farmers won't have their own computers; instead, they will use "time-sharing" computer centers, which will be linked to keyboards and print-out devices in their farm offices.

27

Farm machinery as well as management is also likely to be automated in the future as planting and tilling become more precise and harvesting comes to include more processing and packaging operations. Numerical tape-controlled programs will direct unmanned machines over fields in predetermined patterns, International Harvester's Mr. Fife predicts. Sensing devices similar to space telemetry systems will relay information on field and crop conditions to a computer, which will be able to send back orders instantaneously to speed up or slow down operations, alter the depth at which seeds are being planted and regulate the intensities with which fertilizer is being applied.

Geneticists will breed plants so they mature at the same time, Mr. Fife hopes. Giant harvesters could then not only pick such food crops as peas but could shell, grade, package and freeze them in the same operation. When finished, the harvesters could roar down the highway at the speed of trucks to deliver the produce to transportation depots for direct dispatch to retail warehouses while it was still in a fresh-from-the-farm state.

High land values may eventually make it worthwhile for some farmers and ranchers to move their operations into multilevel structures. Besides utilizing land more fully, indoor farming would raise production by permitting the raising of crops year-round.

R. Louis Ware, a Chicago engineering consultant,

sees the possibility of huge skyscraper "factories" located in major cities for the production of tomatoes, lettuce and other truck produce. The plants might be grown in trays of chemical solutions or synthetic "soils." Carefully controlled doses of carbon dioxide and artificial light would speed growth and insure uniformity. Proximity to market would enhance what Mr. Ware terms the "superflavor" of products grown in such an environment.

Controlled-environment breeding and raising of livestock is almost a certainty. Black, Sivalls and Bryson Incorporated, a Kansas City agricultural equipment concern, recently began marketing the "bacon bin," a fully mechanized facility for raising hogs. The two-story circular structure contains wedge-shaped pens for 46 sows and 450 hogs. Feed and water are deposited in the pens by a rotating auger, and waste-disposal systems under the slatted floors permit farmers to liquidize and store manure for possible use on fields. Temperature controls allow the hogs, whose weight-gaining ability is impaired by heat, to gain more weight on less feed.

J. T. Kenneally, chairman of the Kansas City firm, claims the farmer need spend only 10 minutes or so a day looking after his hogs. In the future, he says, hog production may be limited to a few score big producers, each of whom will raise up to a million swine at a time in neatly arranged rows of "bacon bins."

Food technologists say the trend to uniformity and

29

precision in farm production will be paralleled at the processing level by a continuation of the trend to "convenience" foods requiring minimal preparation. More food will be pre-cooked and packaged in individual portions. When a family sits down to dinner, each person will be able to have a different menu, without putting the cook to extra work.

Food companies also are experimenting with numerous methods for extending the shelf-life of perishable products, making frequent trips to the supermarket unnecessary.

Many food technologists believe freeze-drying, which removes the water from a product after it has been frozen, will be as common in the year 2000 as canning is today. Vegetables, fruits and even meat could be stored for weeks or months on a shelf, resuming their original qualities within seconds after they come in contact with liquid.

Another preservation technique, which has been approved by the Food and Drug Administration for canned bacon and for processing wheat to prevent fungus or microbe infestation, is irradiation. Raw food placed in a field of ionizing radiation remains sterile for an extended period of time, eliminating spoilage from bacteria. Technologists now are working to overcome the adverse effect irradiation has on taste.

Pondering the kitchen of the future, General Electric Company conjures up a vision of an automated food preparation system. One section would store freeze-dried or frozen foods. Another would consist of a microwave oven. To order a meal, the housewife would simply punch out a few instructions, and the food would then be transferred from the storage compartments to the oven at proper intervals and cooked so that everything would be ready for serving in the correct order.

A few problems remain to be solved, of course. For example, a microwave oven doesn't turn cooked foods their usual colors; a well-done steak still looks raw. But food experts are convinced such obstacles won't prevent drastic changes in the kitchen. Comments Swift and Company's Mr. Murphy: "By the year 2000, we'll have eliminated the pot and the pan."

—THOMAS J. BRAY

Computers:

The Impersonal Genie

It's 1980. A motorist is barreling along an eight-lane freeway. Traffic is light, so he nudges his car five, ten, then twenty miles an hour over the speed limit. No police car with flashing light and screaming siren appears on his tail, and he arrives at his destination without a care in the world.

The next day he is notified by the police that his car was involved in a speeding violation and that whoever was driving is due in court. The infraction had been observed by an electronic device that measured the car's speed, noted the license number and flashed the information to a police computer. The computer plucked the name and address of the license-plate holder from its memory and printed it out, along with details of the offense.

Certainly this is fast, efficient law enforcement—and entirely within the realm of technical feasibility. But the prospect of being nabbed by an all-knowing assemblage of transistors and circuitry has disturbing aspects for some people. Their doubts about computerized cops suggest something of a general mood of ambivalence often found among those who have pondered the role of the computer over the next few decades.

Without question, computers will bring many benefits. They will increase factory and office productivity. They will signal new economic trends more quickly. They will store vast amounts of information about law, medicine, science and other fields, with instant access to any bit of needed data available to thousands of widely scattered persons via teletypewriter links. They will serve as invaluable educational tools, and they will permit lightning solution of scientific and technical problems that for all practical purposes would be insoluble otherwise. In all these areas, computers will become easier to use; in the works are machines that could even follow spoken instructions.

On the negative side is the prospect of an extension of the impersonalization that often seems to accompany the introduction of computers. The sort of frustrations already encountered by a customer who feels he has been incorrectly billed by a store with computerized bookkeeping could become commonplace in other areas of life. How, for example, do you explain to a police computer that you were speeding because a passenger was suddenly taken ill and needed immediate attention?

Impersonalization caused by computers could also ruin some jobs, a number of observers assert. Dean

33

Champion, a University of Tennessee sociologist, recently went so far as to forecast that many employes of computer-run plants, where a worker frequently will find himself assigned to an isolated station with the task of watching automated machines, will be driven to alcoholism. He reasons that the lone worker will miss the companionship of laboring alongside others on the assembly line and consequently will spend more leisure hours in bars.

Then there is the privacy issue. Already considerable amounts of information on individuals—their incomes, credit ratings, bank balances and tax payments—have accumulated in business and government computer systems. Now moves are afoot to speed this trend. A Federal commission has proposed a nationwide employment service that would use a computer to store information on job openings and on detailed characteristics for job seekers. The Budget Bureau is considering a computerized national data center that would collect information on millions of Americans from the Census Bureau, the Internal Revenue Service and other United States agencies.

Such data storehouses obviously would offer advantages; in particular, the computerized employment service—viewed as a certainty by the 1980s—might cut jobless rolls. But critics fear officials might be tempted to pry too deeply into personal matters or to use information improperly. For such reasons, Representative

Cornelius F. Gallagher, a New Jersey Democrat who heads a House subcommittee that has been looking into the question of Federal invasion of privacy, finds the proposal for a national data center "appalling."

"We cannot be certain that such dossiers would always be used by benevolent people for benevolent purposes," warns the Congressman.

Concern about possible harmful effects of computers on society clearly is not going to stop their use from steadily widening. But it could at least lead to some legal curbs on the ways they can be used.

For example, Charles A. Reich, a Yale University professor of Constitutional law, urges several safeguards for individuals if the national data center is established. Among them would be rules prohibiting the Government from asking certain questions, such as a man's religious beliefs; restricting information to the agency that originally obtained it; and giving a person the right to know what information has been supplied about him and its source, plus the opportunity to rebut inaccurate data.

Computers are multiplying at a rapid rate. There were fewer than 1,000 in the United States in 1956. By 1967 over 30,000 were in operation. Radio Corporation of America, which makes computers, predicts the total will reach 85,000 by 1975 and 150,000 by 1985. By the turn of the century, there will be 220,000 computers in the United States, RCA forecasts.

Computers' great advantage over human brains or simple calculating machines lies in their enormous capacity for storage of information and in their ability to process masses of data at speeds measured in billionths of a second. Almost any sort of information, whether expressed in numbers or words, can be converted into coded electric pulses and fed into a computer. The computer stores the pulses on magnetic cores or other devices.

In response to highly detailed sets of instructions, known as programs, the computer draws specific bits of information from its memory and manipulates them in almost any way desired, whether the aim is to total a department store customer's charges over a month or to pinpoint a spacecraft's splashdown zone. The results, either in numbers or words, can be printed out or displayed on a screen. They can also be converted into electrical pulses that directly activate machinery.

One key to increasing applications for computers is simplification of the methods for feeding data and processing instructions into a computer. At present, data is almost invariably put onto punched cards, punched paper tape or magnetic tape. Instructions must be written in special computer language. Thus, translating material into forms a computer can handle requires considerable training.

Efforts are under way now to come up with equipment that will enable anyone to "talk" to a computer, with little or no special training. To this end, several new types of "input" devices are being introduced or are under development.

One relatively new input device is a typewriter-like console with which a computer user can simply type information into a computer. Another recent development is the use of push-button telephones to feed data into a computer over telephone lines. For auto designers and others who work with visual representations, computer technologists have devised a system for drawing with a "light pen" on a screen that looks like a television set; lines traced on the screen can be converted to mathematical formulas and stored in the computer's memory.

Optical scanning, or reading, machines that can translate a few styles of print into electrical pulses a computer can understand are already in use. Utilities use them, for example, to transfer data from bill stubs into a computer.

On the horizon are scanning machines that will be able to read any kind of printing and even legible script. These are expected to give computers the capability for almost instantaneous language translation—a capability that scientists and others who must keep abreast of foreign publications would find invaluable. Perhaps by the late 1970s input devices that can understand the human voice will be ready.

Paralleling the improvement of input equipment will

37

be a switch to ordinary language for computer programs. Some computer men say that within 10 years it will be possible to write many programs in everyday English. Such a development will enable programers to write instructions faster, thereby increasing their productivity and making more types of programs available. It also will mean that a researcher or businessman won't have to learn a complex jargon or go through an intermediary to communicate with a computer.

Besides becoming easier to use, computers are getting cheaper. In 1957 it cost $130 a month to lease a computer with enough capacity to store one million characters (a character is a single number or letter). The same storage capacity in 1967 cost $8.75 a month to rent. Some computer men see a monthly charge of 10 cents by the 1980s.

Computers also are becoming more compact as miniaturization of components progresses. This trend means that computers that once filled rooms can now be placed atop desks or aboard spacecrafts. The storage section of one average-sized model of the early 1950s filled 153 cubic feet. Now the same amount of information can be squeezed into 3.3 cubic feet. New developments in circuitry are expected to reduce this to less than one cubic foot by the 1980s.

Despite the trend to compactness and lower costs, it's unlikely everyone will have his own computer any time soon. Instead, the prospect is for various types of computer networks, with central computers linked to many terminals by cable or microwave.

The growth of "time-sharing" computer networks is a certainty, say the experts. Much like the electric power station feeding electricity to thousands of customers, time-sharing computers will be connected to teletypewriters or TV-like display panels in factories, offices, schools and perhaps even homes. The users will be charged for computer services just as they are now billed by electric utilities.

General Electric Company already has set up a time-sharing computer service in New York City that is considered a forerunner of things to come. A computer at the GE Information Processing Center is hooked up, via telephone lines and teletypewriters, to 100 clients—among them, a management consultant, a medical researcher, a publishing representative, an investment research specialist, a small businessman and a group of engineering students.

The customers employ the computer for everything from bookkeeping to the solution of highly complex scientific, technical and economic problems. There is never any waiting because the machine operates at such fantastic speeds.

Other sorts of computer networks are possible. Robert Fano, who directs a computer time-sharing setup for engineering faculty and students at Massachusetts Institute of Technology, envisions systems linking school computers to students' homes. Assignments programed in the computer would be printed out on a teletypewriter in the home. The student would transmit answers back to the computer, which would check them and either repeat troublesome points or move on to the next assignment. Such an arrangement would let each student proceed at his own pace.

Some computer makers predict that by the late 1970s a new system of credit based on computer networks will have started replacing cash and checks. The heart of the system will be a bank computer hooked up to homes, stores, utilities and employers in a community. One bank's computers will be interconnected with other banks' computers.

The possibilities of such a system are varied. By punching a keyboard in its office, a factory could credit a worker's weekly paycheck to his bank account. When the employe shops, he could pay for purchases by having a store signal his bank's computer to transfer funds from his account to the store's. Eventually, individuals might pay bills for utilities and rent through computer hookups to their homes. The theoretical advantage of all this would be a great saving of time and paper work in conducting financial transactions.

The Bank of Delaware and a chain of four shoe stores in Wilmington have been cooperating since March 1966 in a limited test of "electronic credit." Some 200 account holders at the bank have been given special identification cards. If one of these persons buys a pair of shoes at one of the chain's outlets, he presents his card to the clerk, who inserts it in an automatic dialing device attached to a push-button phone and punches out the charge.

The card causes an identifying signal to be transmitted to the computer, and a recorded voice reports back over the phone whether the shopper has enough funds in his account to cover the purchase. If the funds are sufficient, the computer deducts the price of the shoes from the customer's account and credits it to the chain's account. "It has been very satisfactory so far," says a bank spokesman.

A Federal study group sees a strong likelihood that computer networks for the storage and transmission of medical data will be in operation within a decade or two. The system would be built around computers at regional Government health centers. In these would be stored individual medical histories of all citizens, along with exhaustive general medical information, such as patterns of symptoms for various ailments. The computers would be linked to doctors' offices and hospitals.

The setup would permit physicians to obtain instant medical profiles of patients. It also would aid in diagnosis of unusual cases; the doctor could feed a patient's symptoms into the computer, which would promptly respond with a list of the most likely causes.

"The computer will detect patterns that may not

41

have been apparent to the doctor," says Evon C. Greanias, who is guiding development of a medical information system at International Business Machines Corporation. "It won't make decisions for the doctor. But it will analyze information and save a lot of the doctor's time."

All computer experts agree the use of computers to simulate reality is sure to grow rapidly. This technique involves construction of a mathematical "model" of real behavior or conditions in a computer. It permits researchers to investigate matters that would be impossible or too costly to study in actuality. Already computers have simulated the flights of spacecraft and nuclear attacks.

One important trend for the future is likely to be simulation in the economic field. At the local level, a bank could create an economic model of a marketing area; it would contain information about population, age groups, income levels and buying habits. This could aid businessmen.

"Take a hardware merchant thinking of opening a store in the bank's neighborhood," says an IBM specialist in the use of computers in financial fields. "He'll ask the bank if it thinks he can make a go of it. The computer will help in providing the answer."

The Commerce Department and the Brookings Institution are both developing computer models of the United States economy. It's hoped that within a decade highly detailed models that shed new light on the work-ings of the economy will be available. Such models would show, among other things, how gross national product, personal income and employment would respond to a cut in Government spending, a rise in business plant and equipment outlays or an income tax reduction. Such foreknowledge would help Government economic officials make sound decisions.

Computers also are likely to find uses in tackling social problems, such as air and water pollution, inadequate mass transit and traffic congestion. The advantage of a computer here is that it can juggle many interrelated variables and evaluate the effect of various courses of action in a fraction of the time it would take human beings. For example, to help plan for road and transit needs, a computer could weigh such factors as present traffic patterns, the impact of future residential and business development on traffic, public preferences for private autos as against mass transit, the deterrent effect of tolls for road use and the effect of fare cuts on transit patronage.

Most of the chores performed by computers in the business world today are routine clerical assignments such as preparation of payrolls or customers' bills. "But the really significant use of the computer in the coming years will be in giving the head of the company a total picture in graphic form of what his company is doing right now," says Louis Rader, a GE vice president.

43

Information about incoming orders, sales, inventories, expenses and production schedules will be fed into a central company computer from scattered offices. The essential data will be relayed from the computer to the display panel in the chief executive's office. "With up-to-date information he can make a quicker assessment of the situation," says Mr. Rader. "It will cut out waste."

Many of the decisions that middle-management men now make will be made almost automatically by a computer; for example, if a manufacturer's inventory of finished goods declines to a specified level, a computer will print out a production order. This prospect has led some people to conclude the middle-management level will just about disappear. But not everyone agrees. Jay W. Forrester, a professor at MIT's Alfred P. Sloan School of Management, asserts:

"The computer will change the nature of his work. Right now a great deal of the middle manager's work is routine and repetitive, the kind a computer can do. In the future, the middle manager will handle more creative tasks. Perhaps more of them will handle personnel problems, such as motivations of employes. Or more of them will be thinking of new ways of doing business."

In the manufacturing process the computer's major triumphs to date have been in the petroleum, chemical and metals industries. Production in these fields usually consists of a continuous flow of liquid, dry or molten substances easily handled automatically, and such processes are ideal for control by computers. Instruments monitor flow, temperature and other variables and flash data to the computer, which is programed to decide when control adjustments are necessary and to send out signals making required changes in settings.

Nobody really knows if the manufacture of automobiles, tires or rocking chairs can be programed into a computer to the extent that human hands become insignificant. But computer technologists say factory automation definitely will make important advances in the 1970s. In particular, they say that computers will take over the control of materials handling conveyors, drilling machines and machines for testing the end product.

An IBM plant in Endicott, New York, that is run almost entirely by a computer demonstrates how automation can cut costs and raise productivity. The plant makes electronic circuit cards that perform the logical and arithmetical operations in computers—so, in effect, the computer helps make other computers.

The IBM plant produces many types and sizes of circuit cards. The computer sees that conveyors get each card to the right machine at the right time and that the machine performs the right operation on it. It controls the drilling machines that make holes in the cards, the testing machines that insure the holes are in

45

the proper place and the insertion machines that place small components in the holes.

IBM says the automated assembly lines reduce scrappage and improve quality. The company estimates that computer control of the Endicott plant permits production of circuit cards at half what they would cost with conventional hand operations. Moreover, says IBM, the automated system enables it to respond to market demand for different types of circuits two to three times faster than would be possible otherwise; with computer control there is no need to shut down production and shift personnel about when changing the product mix.

The automated circuit card plant employs only a fraction of the production workers that would be needed without automation. The sight of production lines without people is another of the considerations that sometimes give rise to ambivalent feelings about computers. Some observers, particularly in union circles, fear widespread unemployment will result inevitably from increased use of computers in industry.

But others say there can be no clear-cut answer at this point. Logically, it would seem that if industry comes to rely almost totally on computers to guide production operations, there simply would not be enough jobs to go around, unless the work week were drastically reduced.

Up till now, however, workers displaced by automation have generally been absorbed by the expanding economy, and some economists think this will continue to be the case for the foreseeable future. Computer makers themselves note that their industry has created some 250,000 new jobs and that the total will grow.

Even in some fields where controversy over the introduction of computers would seem unlikely, there are those who doubt the amazing machines will be an unmixed blessing. Some doctors and hospital officials, for example, indicate they might not be willing to hand over patient records to computers to which others would have access; making such information freely available, they fear, might lead to a rise in malpractice suits.

Some observers maintain that computer networks set up by banks or by time-sharing data-processing centers also have their alarming aspects. What would happen, they ask, if a computer linking thousands of users were programed incorrectly? Most likely, a monumental snarl would ensue. Bills would be deducted from the wrong bank accounts. The boss' paycheck would be credited to the office boy. The solution to a stress problem posed by an engineer would clack out on the doctor's teleprinter.

—STANLEY PENN

Communications:

The World-Wide Hookup

By the year 2000 you will be able to do just about everything but shake hands or kiss your wife via electronic communications.

You will, for example, be able to sit in your office and hold a face-to-face chat with a business associate on the other side of the globe. While you're talking, you can instantaneously transmit a facsimile of a blueprint or contract for his inspection.

From your home in the United States you will be able to examine—in color—a painting up for sale at a London gallery. Or you can help your school-age son with his essay on the causes of World War I by transmitting a request for a bibliography on the subject to the local library's computer, which would respond by causing a reading list to be printed out on a device in your home.

All these things are possible with today's technology. Indeed, facsimile transmission and "picture phones"— though the images aren't in color yet—are already in limited use. What researchers envision over the next three decades or so is the creation of a vast network of facilities that will put present technology to work and make instant audio and visual communications available world-wide. This same network will also enable computers, which will be playing a much greater role in business, government and science than they do now, to "talk" to each other to exchange masses of data at incomprehensible speeds, as well as to communicate with users located elsewhere.

Satellites, microwave systems and coaxial cables will be the key elements in the communications network expected by the end of the century. The satellites and microwave facilities will flash spoken, visual or computer-coded information, in the form of electrical impulses, over great distances. The coaxial cables will tie individual offices and homes into the network. A single cable might supply a home with as many as 10 commercial and educational television channels, a picture phone and a teletypewriter that could be used to communicate with computers or with other teletypewriters.

"I expect that in every office, and to some extent in every home, you will have a communication facility that can be used for whatever type of communications you want," says John R. Pierce, one of the pioneers of the communications satellite and an executive director of research at American Telephone and Telegraph Company's Bell Telephone Laboratories. "You will have the

49

option of sending text, or speaking or seeing, or perhaps communicating all three ways at once."

Mr. Pierce and other experts agree that demand rather than technological considerations will determine the speed with which communications innovations move from the laboratory to everyday use. "The main concern isn't going to be technological but rather economic and social," says James J. Clerkin Jr., executive vice president of General Telephone and Electronics Corporation. "We could provide many of these futuristic services right now if people wanted them and were willing to pay for them."

People probably won't be willing to pay for "futuristic services" until costs drop far below what communications companies could offer them for now. And the determining factor here is bandwidth—the number of electromagnetic waves, or cycles, that can be transmitted each second in a radio beam. Essentially, the more cycles per second transmitted, the greater the amount of information that can be carried on the beam —and the lower the cost per message.

By way of background, in the days of telegraphy and the Morse code, the only information being transmitted was dots and dashes, and these were sent only as fast as the telegrapher could press the key. Telegraphy required a signal of little more than 60 cycles per second.

In contrast, the human voice, with all its variations in pitch and amplitude, requires a bandwidth of 3,000 cycles per second in order to be reproduced with reasonable faithfulness at the receiving end. The same band needed to carry a single voice can carry more than a score of telegraphic messages.

In United States broadcasting a black-and-white television picture consists of 525 lines that change 30 times a second. To transmit such a picture requires a bandwidth of 4,250,000 cycles per second, many times that required for the voice. In engineers' jargon, television is usually called "broadband" communication, as opposed to the "narrow band" transmission used for voice only.

For some time now the electronic communications network in the United States has been able to provide narrow bandwidths in such quantities and at such low cost that telephone service is available to just about everyone. There are nearly 89 million telephones in the country. Long-distance rates have nosedived; you can call coast to coast for as little as $1, compared with a minimum of $2.50 for a New York-San Francisco call in 1950.

On the other hand, broadband channels, which require coaxial cables or microwave facilities, remain costly. As a result, broadband communications are still available only to large companies with extensive communications needs. The three major television networks say it costs them collectively about $55 million a year to distribute programs to their affiliated stations via the telephone companies' microwave network.

51

In coming decades, however, the capacity of the communications network will expand so greatly that broadband communications eventually will be as plentiful and cheap as telephone service is now. It is this trend that will make picture phones, facsimile and other advanced communications methods increasingly practical and economic. First they will be used by businesses, says Mr. Pierce of Bell Labs, and then as rates drop they will move into homes.

Communications satellites will play a major role in increasing the communications network's capacity. The satellites can transmit microwaves over long distances. Since microwaves transmit in billions of cycles per second, they provide tremendous bandwidth.

Until now, however, microwave transmission has been limited by the microwave characteristic of always traveling in straight lines instead of following the earth's curvature. This has necessitated relay towers every 30 miles or so to bend the microwave beam around the earth. But a single communications satellite hovering 22,300 miles above the equator can pick up a microwave beam from any transmitter in its "view," which covers a third of the globe, and relay the signal to a receiver anywhere in this area.

Present communications satellites are tiny compared to those engineers look for by the turn of the century. Communications Satellite Corporation's Early Bird satellite, now in position over the Atlantic, can relay 240 telephone conversations simultaneously or one television picture. Comsat already has ordered satellites with a capacity equivalent to 1,200 telephone circuits for use in the international communications satellite system. For the 1970s it has proposed a domestic United States satellite system that would use four satellites with combined capacity to relay simultaneously 16 color television programs, plus thousands of telephone, telegraph and facsimile messages.

Satellites with capacities equivalent to at least 60,000 telephone circuits are likely by 2000, according to Joseph V. Charyk, president of Comsat. With each increase in capacity, he explains, the cost of a single circuit drops. As a result, he says, "the cost per channel will become ridiculously low."

Mr. Charyk predicts that every large city will have its own satellite ground terminal. Thus, "satellites will connect large metropolitan centers on a global scale," he says.

The satellite ground terminal will tie into an elaborate system of broadband coaxial cable links to offices and homes throughout the city. The cable hookups would probably come in stages, with people who live near the heart of a city being wired into the system before residents of outlying areas.

Engineers say the idea of broadband communications links going into homes isn't at all farfetched. The starting point would probably be cable networks to distribute TV programs to homes. Already more than 2 million American homes are receiving television over cables connected to community antennas. Such hookups, which give small-town residents a much wider choice of programs than they would have otherwise, seem certain to increase. In major cities, cable networks designed to improve television reception are growing. Also, there's a chance that eventually pay-TV will stir enough interest to bring about more cable links to urban homes.

In short, says Edmund A. Laport, director of communications engineering at Radio Corporation of America's Sarnoff Laboratories in Princeton, New Jersey, "just as the nation was wired for telephone, it could be wired for television."

The next step would be to connect the community antenna or pay-TV cable systems to satellite ground terminals and to local communications facilities. Thus, it's theorized, would be born the network of broadband communications channels that would make global picture phones and facsimile service possible. Ultimately all forms of communication, including the telephone and transmissions between computers, would use the intracity cable system. It "will become economic to put all communications into one pipe," says General Telephone's Mr. Clerkin.

Even though no scientific breakthroughs are needed to create the network Mr. Clerkin and others envision, no one rules out spectacular new developments in basic technology in the communications field. Some of the most intriguing possibilities are presented by the laser.

The laser is a device that produces a beam of "pure" light. If techniques can be worked out to make use of it, this light beam could offer undreamed of capacity for carrying communications. Whereas the microwaves currently used for broadband communications have frequencies in the billions of cycles per second, laser light waves come in frequencies of hundreds of trillions of cycles per second. A visible red laser beam, for example, has a frequency of about 430 trillion cycles per second.

"In just the small portion of (the light spectrum) that is visible to people there is about a million times more room for messages than there is in the entire range of frequencies we now use for communications," says a Bell Labs report. And this doesn't take into account the invisible infrared and ultraviolet portions of the spectrum.

If scientists could find a way to use laser beams to transmit sounds and pictures, the cost per communications channel would plummet. But researchers aren't at all sure they can master laser technology by 2000. The obstacles are numerous. As yet no one has devised an efficient method of putting messages onto a laser beam that takes full advantage of its tremendously high frequencies. Moreover, since a light beam won't go through buildings, clouds, fog or even very far through ordinary atmosphere, laser pipes must be developed and techniques must be devised for bending the pipe-enclosed beam around corners, over mountains and through valleys.

Forecasting the course of technology is generally easier than predicting what communications services people will want and how soon these services can be supplied at reasonable prices, communications specialists say. Some communications innovations that are technically feasible right now stumble over economics, they note.

Mr. Clerkin, for instance, recalls that General Telephone recently tested an automatic device for reading water meters. It was attached to home meters, and periodically it would transmit the meter reading through the telephone system to the water company, making it unnecessary for a man to come around to read meters. The setup worked, but "it fell through on economics," says Mr. Clerkin. "The gadget that went on the meter was too costly." If the cost could be brought down, of course, automatic meter reading might win acceptance in the future.

Communications men are confident that demand for picture phones and facsimile will be high enough—and costs low enough—to bring about widespread introduction of the services sometime before the end of this century. But they won't be much more precise than this.

Mr. Charyk of Comsat suggests that many business conferences of the future will take place with the aid of picture phones and facsimile. Even the signing of contracts could take place with the participants thousands of miles apart, he says. A copy of a contract could be signed at one end and a faithful picture flashed to the other party by facsimile. This would be signed, and a copy transmitted back. Both parties, who would be able to observe each other all the time over the picture phone, would have signed copies.

Television and facsimile links between remote individuals are obviously years away, but some of the advanced ground facilities that will be needed to handle future communications needs are already far along. The heart of these facilities is a new electronic switching system that is beginning to replace the electro-mechanical setup that has served till now.

With electro-mechanical switching the dialing of a telephone number triggers magnets that in turn cause switches to flip. Making a connection with this system is a matter of seconds. Adding a new telephone service —such as direct-distance dialing—requires extensive rewiring.

With the electronic system, the switching equipment is basically a computer. Connections are made in hundredths of seconds by electronic pulses rather than by the movement of switches. More important than the speed, however, is the ease with which services can be added or changed with electronic switching. All that's necessary is to feed instructions for new services into the computer's memory. Essentially, these instructions

57

specify that when certain combinations of digits are dialed, the memory directs the machine to establish a particular connection.

Though the electronic system is designed for a day when communications loads will be much heavier and services more diverse than at present, its capabilities are already being demonstrated in a limited way.

In some communities where telephone companies have installed electronic switching customers can get "speed dialing" service. A customer's most frequently called numbers are inserted in the computer memory. From then on, whenever he dials one or two digits, the machine automatically dials the complete number in a fraction of a second. Another new service allows a departing family to dial a series of numbers and thereby instruct the computer to switch all incoming phone calls to the place they will be visiting.

Bell Labs researchers constantly toy with schemes for other new phone services made possible by electronic switching. "One idea some of our guys are speculating about, for example, is a 'baby-sitter's hot line,'" says Raymond W. Ketchledge, executive director of the electronic switching division at Bell Labs. A harried baby-sitter would pick up the phone. If she didn't dial in four or five seconds, a number the parents had fed into the computer before going out would ring automatically.

— JERRY E. BISHOP

Energy:

Doing the Work

The collection of big concrete bubbles and low, windowless buildings nestles by the sea. There is no noise, and not a trace of smoke rises into the air. The absence of visible utility lines makes it appear unconnected to the outside world.

But through underground transmission cables it pours out almost 12 million kilowatts, enough to supply the 1966 requirements of the entire state of Illinois. As an almost incidental by-product, it daily converts more than a billion gallons of salt water into fresh water, enough to meet New York City's needs today.

This awesomely efficient facility is a nuclear-powered electricity-generating plant of the year 2000 as envisioned by engineers of Westinghouse Electric Corporation. Several technological hurdles remain to be cleared before such a plant can be built, but experts at Westinghouse and elsewhere are convinced the problems can be solved. And they say that such huge plants will be essential to fill the greatly increased power demands expected by the end of the century.

59

By then Americans are likely to be using three times as much energy as at present. This includes energy of all kinds—from that needed to light a living room or cook a steak to that used to move a car or operate a steel rolling mill. "Our national economy," remarks Carl E. Reistel Jr., former chairman of Humble Oil and Refining Company, "is marked by an insatiable thirst for energy."

Part of the increase in the demand for energy will stem from the anticipated 70% rise in the United States population between now and 2000. But most of it will result from increased per-capita use of power, chiefly in the form of electricity.

Electric heating elements embedded in driveways will melt snow the instant it hits, for example. Roadways, including alleys and interstate highways, will be brilliantly lit, cutting accidents and crime. The coldest weather won't stop the home owner from barbecuing on his patio, protected from the elements by curtains of heated air. In factories, automatic machines and materials handling equipment will all but eliminate physical labor, while huge electric-powered lasers or electron beams will cut and shape metal in a fraction of the time now needed.

Despite the surge in demand for energy, the supply is expected to be ample in the years ahead. Moreover, it will cost less than it does today because the means of producing it will become more efficient.

Researchers say the Earth still holds enough of the "fossil fuels"—coal, oil and gas—to keep homes and factories humming for centuries. Undeveloped sources of water power are also available in many parts of the world; Alaska alone has an unused waterpower potential of more than 10 million kilowatts of electricity.

And ultimately there will be almost limitless supplies of power from nuclear plants, expected eventually to be the cheapest source of energy almost everywhere on the globe. The long-term goal in the nuclear field is a fusion reactor. It would duplicate the physical process of the sun, using fuel obtainable from ordinary sea water. There is enough of that around to supply the Earth with energy at a thousand times the current rate of consumption for 20 million years, estimates Amasa S. Bishop, head of fusion research for the Atomic Energy Commission.

Harold S. Walker Jr., assistant managing director of the American Gas Association, maintains future energy needs will be so high that "there's going to be plenty of room for all current forms of energy." His own industry is working hard to try to insure that gas stays in the running; the fuel cell, which uses gas to generate electricity, is one manifestation of this effort.

But it is obvious that there will be a steady change in the relative importance of various energy sources, just as there has been in the past. A century ago Americans got three-fourths of their energy from burning wood. By 1920 coal had about three-fourths of the energy market. Today oil and gas make up 70% or so of the raw fuel used to produce energy in the United States. By 2000 nuclear fuels will be moving toward a commanding position.

The uses to which particular types of energy are put will also change. A General Electric Company scientist predicts improved batteries will permit electric cars to start making a comeback by the early 1970s, mainly as small vehicles for running errands in town.

W. Perry Bollinger, Westinghouse's transportation division manager, forecasts that by 2000 all railroads will be electrified because "the economics will become overpowering by that time." Some dissenters suggest the $300,000-per-mile cost of electrification may deter railroads from converting; only a little more than 1% of the 375,000 miles of track in the United States is now electrified. The skeptics on electrification suggest gas turbine engines may prove a more attractive and economical alternative to diesels. But Mr. Bollinger and others contend the lower operating costs of electrics will cause them to win out in the end. The electrics' cost advantages stem mainly from their high speeds and the elimination of the dead weight of diesel fuel and bulky diesel engines.

Nuclear power plants seem certain to start replacing oil-fired boilers in merchant ships in substantial numbers before too long. An official of the Federal Maritime

Administration says that by 2000 the nuclear ships "will be counted in the hundreds." They will be big, displacing 40,000 tons or more (the only nuclear merchant ship today, the Savannah, displaces 13,600 tons). They will average more than 30 knots, compared with 10 to 15 knots for conventional present ships. Besides the speed, the big attraction of a nuclear ship is low fuel costs; it will cost two-thirds as much to carry one ton of cargo one mile in a nuclear vessel as in a conventional ship.

As far as the individual consumer is concerned, the biggest change in the energy field will be the expanding role of electricity. Today electricity provides just over 20% of the energy used by the consumer, compared with about 10% in 1930. By 1980, the Edison Electric Institute estimates, the proportion will be 30% and by 2000 it will reach somewhere between 40% and 50%. "We see no end to the trend," says Edwin Vennard, a vice president of the trade group.

Fred Borch, GE president, calculates that per-capita use of electricity in 2000 could go as high as 27,000 kilowatt hours a year, compared with about 6,000 today. The kitchen is one place where electricity is expected to make gains. Gas is now used in more homes than electricity for cooking, but electricity is closing the gap and by one estimate, it will be doing the cooking in more than 60% of the nation's homes by 2000.

Home heating is an even more important area of

63

growth for electricity. Home heating is now dominated by oil and gas; only 3% to 4% of the homes in the United States are heated electrically. But Resources for the Future, a private research group, forecasts that by the end of the century 30% of American homes will use electric heating. Edison Electric Institute goes much further and exuberantly predicts that by 2000 "virtually all" homes will have electric heating.

The institute's prediction evokes considerable skepticism, however. Says a gas industry spokesman: "Electricity would have to get every new home in the United States and that would mean the oil and gas people would have to roll over and play dead."

Oil is certain to be badly hurt, though, with its share of the heating market likely to drop to 15%, half its present level, by 2000. Coal furnaces, still found in around 300,000 American homes, will have disappeared almost completely by 2000. But electricity and gas should wage a fierce competitive battle for some time to come, and one likely result is that the consumer will often get a break as electric and gas interests vie with each other. More and more frequently builders will receive subsidies to install one type of appliance instead of another, thereby lowering the ultimate price the home buyer pays. Also, utilities may offer special rates aimed at winning over blocs of home owners.

However vigorously gas resists electricity's inroads, the nation's electric capacity will have to be greatly expanded between now and the end of the century. By the end of 1966, the electric capacity of the United States was about 250 million kilowatts, and use was 1.2 trillion kilowatt hours annually. By 1980, capacities must rise to 525 million kilowatts to meet a demand for nearly 3 trillion kilowatt hours, the Federal Power Commission estimates. By 2000, capacity ought to be between 1.4 billion and 1.6 billion kilowatts and yearly use may reach 8 trillion kilowatt hours.

For electric utilities to expand at this rate would cost them $420 billion by 2000, according to Philip Sporn, former president of American Electric Power Company and now head of its planning committee. The total capital investment of American utilities as of 1962 was $69 billion.

Some people in the gas industry doubt the electric utilities can grow fast enough to keep up with electricity demand. The gas men think their industry can cash in to some extent on the growth in electricity requirements by promoting the use of gas to produce electricity. They urge the installation of gas turbines and, for the future, fuel cells, to supply electric power to one building or a complex of buildings. The waste heat from these devices, they say, can be used as building heat.

Some 300 apartment houses, schools and office buildings in the United States now have their own gas turbines to produce electricity. Looking ahead, gas indus-

65

try spokesmen say the fuel cell, an even more efficient device for using gas to make electricity, will be ready for installation in homes and commercial buildings by 1975. Fuel cells take hydrogen from gas or other sources and oxygen from the air and combine them to produce electricity.

The gas industry claims fuel cells will cut the cost of electricity. Home owners in some areas where electric rates are high, they assert, could save hundreds of dollars a year in electric bills.

But there's a catch—the capital cost of installing a fuel cell. While the owner of an office building or factory might be swayed by the prospect of long-term operating savings, home buyers and builders probably would balk at the extra initial cost of a fuel cell. The Institute of Gas Technology projects the cost of a typical home installation at $1,060. In most cases, says one fuel cell authority, "the consumer won't even have a choice. The builder will want to build the house for the cheapest cost."

Federal Power Commission experts also seem to have their doubts about the future of fuel cells for individual power units. On-site electricity generation has declined from 50% of total capacity prior to World War I to about 10% now, and the FPC believes this downward trend will continue.

The electric utilities' competitive position is likely to be strengthened by a continuation of the drop in electricity's cost. Mr. Vennard of the Edison Electric Institute figures that by 1980 the consumer's cost per kilowatt hour will be from 1.4 to 1.5 cents, compared with the 1965 national average of 1.59 cents. Mr. Sporn of American Electric Power says the cost may drop to only 1 cent per kilowatt hour by 2000.

The electric industry hopes both to drive costs down and obtain needed new capacity by constructing massive central stations with efficiencies far higher than the current average of 33% (this means all but 33% of the energy is now wasted in generating electricity). Coal, which is the fuel used for just over half the generating capacity in the United States now, and gas, which accounts for much of the remainder, will be the fuels at a few of these facilities; in the case of coal, new efficiency-boosting techniques may prolong its attractiveness as an energy source in some areas. But most of the big new power stations will be built around nuclear reactors. One authority predicts that by 2000 all large plants ordered will be atomic and within 20 to 30 years after that the last important coal-fired generating plants probably will be shutting down.

Although reactors can already produce electricity more cheaply than coal in some locations, the 12 atomic energy plants in operation in the United States in 1966 generated only a trickle of power—about 1.8 million kilowatts out of the total United States capacity of 250 million kilowatts. But 36 nuclear plants on order or under construction will add another 25.3 million kilowatts by 1973. By 1980, says Atomic Energy Commission Chairman Glenn Seaborg, atomic energy capacity may reach as much as 110 million kilowatts, a fifth of the total electric capacity the United States is expected to have then. By 2000, Mr. Seaborg continues, nuclear reactors will account for half the nation's electric capacity.

If past experience is any guide, these estimates may prove too conservative. The AEC has already been forced to revise its forecasts twice, and the new estimates are more than double ones made just four years ago. Makers of atomic energy equipment say even they have been startled by the high rate of orders recently; through the first nine months of 1966, more than 50% of the electric capacity ordered for installation in the United States was for nuclear plants.

Utilities now are buying water reactors that use the heat from the splitting of uranium atoms to convert water to steam, which turns turbines to generate electricity. This type of reactor, perhaps with certain improvements, is likely to be built into the 1980s.

By 1985, "breeder" reactors should be ready. Breeders are considered essential to stretch uranium supplies, which appear to be limited. The breeder reactor eases this supply problem by creating more fissionable material than it uses.

About 3% of the uranium used to fuel present reactors

is the fissionable type, uranium-235. The rest is uranium-238, a material whose atoms can't be split. In a breeder reactor, however, all the time the uranium-235 is fissioning and producing energy, some of the uranium-238 will slowly be undergoing transformation into plutonium-239, an element that will fission. The AEC's breeder blueprint calls for a reactor able to produce 1.4 pounds of plutonium from uranium-238 for every pound of uranium-235 it "burns" over a 10-to-15-year period.

The way is not yet clear to the building of a breeder reactor. The AEC is leaning toward the use of liquid sodium instead of water in the reactor because it has characteristics that make the breeding process more efficient, but Milton Shaw, head of the AEC's reactor development efforts, says there are engineering problems. For one, sodium must be kept at a high temperature to remain liquid; for another, it reacts violently if it comes in contact with air or water.

Another problem in breeder reactors is that plutonium is a deadly poison, which makes it tricky to handle and fabricate into fuel elements. Because of such difficulties, producing a breeder reactor may well cost up to $1 billion more than the $400 million already spent on the project by the AEC.

Development of a workable breeder reactor will open the way to the huge power complexes envisioned by Westinghouse and others. Preliminary work on such a plant might start in 1980, with completion likely around

69

2000. The complex might consist of four breeder reactors, plus four water reactors or "advanced converter" reactors; the advanced converter models would be similar to breeders but would convert smaller amounts of uranium-238 into plutonium. The power facility might also include one coal or gas-fired turbine; such generating units can be turned on and off more quickly than nuclear equipment.

The water reactors, which would be the first major part of the complex to be built because their technology is far advanced, could be used some of the time for water desalination, a function that explains Westinghouse's choice of a coastal location for its dream plant. With nearby breeder reactors producing more fissionable material than they consume, the uranium shortage that would otherwise make water reactors unsatisfactory for the long term will not be a problem. Mr. Seaborg of the AEC foresees the need for computers "to schedule the flow of fissionable material from one reactor to another."

Fusion is regarded as the last major development in atomic energy possible in this century. Some researchers think there's a chance fusion may prove unattainable. Henry Hurwitz, a GE scientist, says "commercially feasible fusion power by 2000 might cost $2 billion and up." But he adds that he sees only a 10% or so chance that the job could be done for $2 billion and concludes: "It's also conceivable we may never do it."

On the other hand, the AEC's Mr. Bishop is confident that the feasibility of fusion will be demonstrated by the end of the 1970s and that the technology for building commercial fusion plants will be developed by 2000. "Everything points to the likelihood from an economic point of view that controlled (fusion) will be in the ball park with other sources of power," he says.

So far scientists have not learned how to control the fusion process. The course of fusion research has moved in precisely the opposite direction from fission research. Fission power began with controlled reactors, then progressed to the uncontrolled bomb; fusion began with the uncontrolled hydrogen bomb and has never progressed to the controlled stage.

Fusion is the joining of hydrogen atoms to make helium and at the same time release energy; this is the process that goes on continuously on the sun. The ideal fusion reactor would combine two atoms of "heavy hydrogen." These atoms, twice the weight of normal hydrogen, are called deuterium and are found in water.

Fusion requires incredible temperatures—on the order of 100 million degrees. And dealing with these is only one of the difficulties faced by scientists in building a fusion reactor. The biggest problem of all is containing the fusion reaction for the few seconds needed to produce usable power. At present, says Mr. Bishop, "we're still several orders of magnitude away from what we need in confinement time."

71

If scientists can indeed figure out how to build a practical fusion reactor, the power plants that might result would probably dwarf anything on the drawing boards today. "The bigger you make it, the more economical it looks," says one researcher, who says single reactor units with capacities as high as 10 million kilowatts might be possible.

Practical considerations spur the constant search for more efficient, cheaper ways to generate electricity. But at least one important change foreseen in the utility field will stem from an entirely nonutilitarian motive. "By 2000," says M. J. McDonough, a Westinghouse executive, "all transmission and distribution lines will be underground because of the drive for aesthetics."

—WILLIAM D. HARTLEY

Air Travel:

Faster and Easier

The supersonic transport has yet to fly. But the forward thinkers in aerospace already are turning their attention to the hypersonic transport.

The HST, as it's called, could start commercial service in the 1990s. The first versions of the dart-shaped, 250-passenger craft would travel 4,000 miles an hour, fast enough to fly from New York to Hong Kong in two hours. Later HSTs might hit speeds of 6,000 miles an hour.

Aerospace planners see the HST as the ultimate in air travel in this century. But they don't expect it to obsolete other types of aircraft. Rather, they view it as the fastest and costliest of several levels of air service.

Just below it in speed and price will be the supersonic transport, or SST, the 1,400-to-1,800-mile-an-hour jets whose initial models will take to the air starting in 1971. Still slower and cheaper will be mammoth versions of the subsonic jets flying today; by offering cut-rate international fares—perhaps as little as $150 for a New York-London round trip by the late 1970s, for example—these

73

planes could open up foreign travel to a whole new segment of the public. Rounding out air service in the closing decades of the Twentieth Century will be nimble new short-haul craft that can take off or land in the heart of a city but will carry more passengers and operate far more cheaply than today's helicopters.

The greater size and speed of tomorrow's planes should mean the number of planes aloft won't grow as fast as passenger and cargo volume. The airlines' passenger business is expected to more than quadruple between 1967 and 1980, while cargo business, by one estimate, should increase more than 15 times as capacity climbs and rates fall. But the skies will become sufficiently congested so that elaborate new systems for electronic control of aircraft movements will be essential. New arrangements at airports for handling passengers and their baggage also will be needed.

Aviation old-timers caution that some past attempts to discern the future of flight have missed the mark. In the late 1940s it was widely forecast that thousands of Americans would soon be flying their own helicopters to work or to the golf course, but the machines' high initial and operating costs have limited them to commercial, military and executive use. A $1 billion Government program to develop a nuclear-powered plane folded after it was stymied by the problems raised by heavy reactor shielding, though military demands for huge sky freighters or antimissile radar picket planes with practically limitless range could eventually revive the project.

One idea bandied about nowadays—the use of rockets to move people at speeds of 15,000 miles an hour—has already been ruled out by most aerospace authorities, at least for the commercial market. "We could deliver people to far distant points in a few minutes, of course," says an officer of a leading aerospace company. "But we doubt that civilian passengers would ever be willing to endure the discomfort of high acceleration and deceleration necessary for the trip."

Aerospace industry officials agree that the rate at which new developments in air transportation come along will hinge in large measure on Government policy. They note that the military has sponsored the development of every large American jet engine. And they point out that work on the SST could not have gone forward if Washington had not consented to help industry bear the immense financial burden entailed in developing the plane; of the $2 billion-plus development cost, the Government probably will put up 75% to 90%.

Even more Government backing will be needed to move the hypersonic transport beyond the theory stage, say aerospace men. A military version of the craft will almost certainly have to precede the commercial one because of the immense development costs, it's agreed.

This does not mean, however, that research looking

toward hypersonic travel—defined as 4,000 miles an hour and up—is at a standstill. In laboratories of industry and of the National Aeronautics and Space Administration, scientists are seeking to solve the materials and design problems posed by the HST.

Some HST materials, such as titanium, will be similar to those already developed for the SST. But at many points the HST will subject materials to stresses and temperature extremes far beyond anything in the SST, and totally new materials must be found.

As an indication of the temperature problem, friction will heat the leading edge of the HST wing to 2,000 degrees Fahrenheit or more, four or five times the highest temperatures to be reached by the "skin" of the SST; engine temperatures will go even higher. At the opposite extreme, the HST's fuel tanks will have to be able to hold liquid hydrogen with a temperature of minus 423 degrees Fahrenheit, cold enough to shatter ordinary materials.

The performance improvements that can result from advances in materials and design frequently are much more spectacular than the layman might expect. This stems from what the Air Force calls the "cascade" effect, which refers to the tendency for new materials and designs to achieve several important objectives at the same time. This phenomenon explains why aerospace researchers think in terms of great jumps in aircraft speeds rather than a slow, steady rise.

Explaining how the cascade effect might operate in practice, Air Force experts say that a new heat-resistant and extremely strong material might raise the efficiency of a jet engine 40%. But the reduced fuel requirements resulting from the higher efficiency would also cut the size and weight of the tanks and lower takeoff weight. Thus, what started as a 40% gain in engine performance would contribute significantly to improvement in other aspects of the plane's performance.

With the benefits of other applications of new materials and of aerodynamic improvements rippling throughout the aircraft in similar fashion, the end product could be a plane several times more efficient than the most advanced previous models.

Researchers are devoting considerable effort to the development of new heat-resistant materials for jet engines. The turbojet engines of 1967 build up temperatures of slightly over 2,000 degrees, but experts say higher temperatures would greatly increase the efficiency of engines. They expect to reach 2,400 degrees in experimental engines soon and are aiming for temperatures as high as 3,000 degrees in 15 to 20 years.

The engine made by United Aircraft Corporation's Pratt and Whitney division for the Boeing 727 tri-jet puts out five pounds of thrust for each pound of weight. Engine builders already have tested models with ratios of 16 to 1. Some researchers think ratios of 20 to 1 might be achieved by 1975 and of 30 to 1 by 1980.

A number of aerospace authorities are confident major advances in jet engine technology are near. "The United States is on the threshold of a dramatic breakthrough in propulsion which will lead the way for a revolution in aeronautics," asserts J. B. Montgomery, president of Marquardt Corporation, a specialist in highspeed missile and aircraft engines. Declares J. W. Mullen II, president of Texaco Incorporated's research division: "The materials barrier to high temperatures is disintegrating rapidly."

Most of the bets are riding on "composite materials." There are many variations, but most of these consist of fibers of boron, silicon or carbon in a matrix of plastic, steel, aluminum or titanium. Besides displaying remarkable immunity to damage from heat, such combinations are strong and light. It has been estimated that use of a boron fiber and plastic material to replace aluminum alloy and titanium at several points in the new F111 fighter-bomber could cut the plane's weight as much as 3,200 pounds, a 3% reduction.

New types of engines as well as new materials will be needed to attain speeds of 4,000 to 6,000 miles an hour. The most likely candidate is a combination of today's turbojet with the ramjet, an immensely efficient type of supersonic engine that already has been used in experimental craft and in the now discontinued Bomarc missile. The turbojet part of the engine would get the plane off the ground and push it to an altitude of 65,000 feet and a speed of about 2,000 miles an hour, at which point the ramjet would take over.

Researchers say the HST's cruising height of 100,000 feet or more will just about eliminate any sonic boom disturbance on the ground. This would be a distinct advantage over the SST, which will create serious sonic boom problems as it flies along at 65,000 feet and may have to be limited to over-ocean routes unless smaller, less noisy models are developed for overland flights.

The only fuel efficient enough to power the HST would be liquid hydrogen. Now used to power rockets, liquid hydrogen weighs less than one-fourth as much as kerosene or other present-day jet fuels but delivers 2¾ times as much heat and power per pound. A side benefit of supercold hydrogen is that it can be circulated around the aircraft as a coolant to counteract the tremendous skin friction heat.

One catch is that liquid hydrogen is costly, even when its extra power is taken into account. The 1967 price ranges from 50 cents to 70 cents a gallon, though this could be expected to decline sharply with large volume.

Some of the materials that will go into the HST are also extremely expensive, at least at this stage. The boron fibers used in composite materials cost $500 or more a pound, and another type of fibers runs $3,500 a pound. But these prices are likely to drop; a few years ago boron fibers cost $6,000 a pound.

79

Even with decreases in fuel and materials costs, however, HSTs are going to be extremely expensive to build and operate, particularly in their early years. This helps explain why the SST and other planes less swift than the HST are going to be around for a long time. By any standards other than those of aerospace researchers, of course, the SST will provide incredibly fast transportation.

The first SST model to go into service will be the Concorde, being built under joint British and French sponsorship and due in the early 1970s; the Concorde will carry 135 passengers at speeds of 1,450 miles an hour. Coming along in 1975 will be the American SST, which will have a capacity of more than 250 persons and a cruising speed of 1,800 miles an hour. The American SST will make the hop to London in two-and-a-half hours, compared with over six hours for present jet airliners and with just under an hour for the early models of the HST.

Airlines have no firm ideas on fares for supersonic travel, but the general thinking is that a seat on an SST will probably cost about as much as a first-class ticket today. Initial HST fares probably would be substantially higher.

Being a passenger on an SST or an HST won't be too much different from traveling on present jets. Cabins will be laid out similarly, and there won't be any sensation of the increased speeds.

In contrast to the supersonic craft, the subsonic jumbo jets will offer passengers an experience quite different from present jet travel. Boeing Company engineers say the huge size of the planes will give passengers the feeling they are aboard an ocean liner rather than an airplane.

The first of the outsized jets, the Boeing 747, will go into service in 1970. It will have a capacity of up to 490 persons. A few years later still larger planes, capable of carrying as many as 1,000 passengers, may become available. The latter monsters could very well evolve from the C5A military transport Lockheed Aircraft Corporation is developing for the Air Force; Pan American World Airways, for one, has shown interest in such a plane. Ranges of up to 15,000 miles are forecast for the later models of the subsonic giants, compared with upper range limits of 8,000 miles or so for advanced SSTs and 6,000 miles for early HSTs. The "stretched" Douglas DC8's 6,000-mile range is the longest of any plane flying today.

A Boeing mock-up of the 747 has two aisles and groups of center seats as well as the usual seats beside the windows. The plane will have four or five galleys and about the same lavatory-to-passenger ratio as on present airliners.

American Airlines has publicized plans for a 340-seat version of the 747 that will have a spiral staircase between decks, a theater section, a drawing room and

81

staterooms, in addition to the ordinary seats. Though such a layout sounds intriguing, some advocates of lower fares say that reducing the passenger capacity of the 747 works against the substantial fare cuts the jumbo jets could make possible. But airline officials say that, in any case, they won't be able to offer markedly lower fares on the jumbos for several years after their introduction because of the need to "protect" investments in the present generation of jets.

Exciting as the new long-range jets will be, the average traveler may benefit more from the new short-haul craft capable of operating from landing spaces no larger than a small city parking lot or a pier.

These new transports will be used for trips of up to 500 miles or so, flying from one city center to another and thereby eliminating lengthy ground journeys to outlying airports. They might also be used to travel between downtown areas and the fields for long-range jets, where they would have special landing strips of their own and thus would not tie up regular runways; such a service might whisk travelers from the heart of Washington, D.C., to Dulles International Airport, 26 miles away, in 10 minutes instead of the 40 to 50 minutes it now takes by taxi.

Present helicopters can fulfill some of these functions. But their operating costs are high—10 to 12 cents a seat mile—and their top speed is about 150 miles an hour. The new types of short-haul craft, which will employ tilting wings, fans in the wings or improved rotors, are expected both to cut operating costs and increase speeds when they go into service in the 1970s.

A recent study by the Air Transport Association estimated that the seat-mile cost for such transports would run between 2.8 cents and 4 cents. Speeds might go as high as 500 miles an hour. The ATA envisions a VSTOL—for "vertical or short takeoff and landing"—that could make the trip from Manhattan to the center of Philadelphia in 35 minutes for a fare of $10.50. This compares with two hours and 25 minutes and a total cost of $15.05 (including airport buses) if a traveler takes a jet between the regular airports of the two cities today.

Lockheed is working on a VSTOL that it believes may even beat the ATA operating cost estimates, lowering the seat-mile figure to 1.5 cents. The Lockheed craft will combine the characteristics of a helicopter with those of an ordinary fixed-wing jet plane.

The rotor would be a new rigid type that eliminates the complex hinging mechanism required by the flapping blades of present helicopters. The rotor would lift the craft vertically off the landing pad, after which two jet engines would take over and drive the craft forward at up to 500 miles an hour. During horizontal flight the rotor blades would fold and retract into the top of the fuselage. When is was time to land, the rotor would go into operation again. The craft could carry 80 to 100 or more passengers.

Some aviation authorities warn that cities should

83

start setting aside VSTOL landing areas now, while the space is still available. Oscar Bakke, the Federal Aviation Agency administrator for the Eastern United States urges New York City planners to provide for small waterfront strips in a lower Manhattan rebuilding program now on the drawing boards. "If they don't and the area is filled with new buildings, the chance will be gone for good," he says.

In the course of a weekend civil defense exercise it was demonstrated that even with the short-takeoff planes flying today it is possible to land and take off close to the heart of New York; planes as large as a 47-passenger transport operated from makeshift 1,000-foot landing strips near the docks and on other vacant property in the city. The success of the exercise prompted New York City to announce it would explore the possibility of using a city-owned pier in lower Manhattan for a VSTOL strip.

Meshing the VSTOLs with the growing fleets of longer-range jets is part of the problem that faces air traffic control planners. A constant flow of VSTOLs is envisioned around major cities, perhaps operating with headways as short as one-and-a-half minutes.

Air traffic control experts say the VSTOLs would probably fly below other airline traffic patterns. This would require better ground control than is now available, but the FAA is working hard to improve equipment and techniques. Improved control for all types of air traffic is essential if time saved by increased speeds is not to be eaten up by takeoff and landing delays. The aim is to let planes operate closer together with no loss of safety and to approach airports when ceilings are lower than present minimums.

What's needed is equipment that will pinpoint aircraft positions far more precisely than is now possible. Within the next few years, better radar gear and devices on board planes that automatically send identification signals to the ground will begin to solve this problem. Further assistance will come from computers, which will instantaneously analyze data on plane movements and plot required turns and altitude changes.

Even with better traffic control, however, some airports are going to reach the maximum allowable congestion before too long. Aircraft traffic at all three metropolitan New York airports, for example, will be at absolute capacity by 1972, according to John Wiley, director of airports for the Port of New York Authority. Though some airline officials argue that the solution for New York's congestion is to shunt personal and business planes to fields other than the three airports used by airlines, Mr. Wiley and a number of others argue that it's urgent that work start immediately on a new major airport to serve New York.

Los Angeles also may need a new field soon to supplement Los Angeles International Airport, already so busy that Mayor Sam Yorty has suggested double-decking the parking lots. Some planners have proposed building two levels for airplane loading and unloading at crowded fields so that more planes could cluster around terminals.

Both airports and airlines will have to devise new passenger-handling procedures before the giant subsonic jets start flying at the end of this decade. Otherwise, with throngs of as many as 1,000 persons boarding and disembarking from single planes, the confusion might be too great.

Fortunately, the big jets will have more than the two doors of the largest present airliners, which should simplify loading and unloading. The Boeing 747 will have four doors, each wide enough for two people. The plane's 340 to 490 passengers probably will be divided into four or five groups, each with different colored tickets and baggage tags corresponding with separate color-designated departure gates and baggage claim areas.

—RICHARD P. COOKE

Space:

Men on Mars

"By the year 2000 we will undoubtedly have a sizable operation on the moon, we will have achieved a manned Mars landing and it's entirely possible we will have flown with men to the outer planets," forecasts Wernher von Braun, the famed rocket expert.

More than a score of other scientists and engineers, directing the United States space program or critically observing it from the sidelines, express similar optimism. These men are acutely aware of the difficulties confronting United States space efforts. But they insist the setbacks bound to occur from time to time should not obscure the immense achievements in five brief years of manned space flights, or dim the vistas for the future. The launching facilities, skilled manpower and basic space technology are already available to accomplish even more challenging and complex tasks than landing man on the moon by the end of this decade.

Here are the major possibilities most United States spacemen foresee for the next few decades:

Early 1970s: Extended lunar exploration, enabling

astronauts to remain on the moon's surface for several weeks and journey miles from their landing site; Earth orbital flights of three months' duration, determining the effects of prolonged weightlessness on man.

Mid-1970s: Landing of automated unmanned craft on Mars to search for signs of life; launching of the nation's first civilian space station, sustaining six astronauts in Earth orbit for a year; initial operation of satellite systems to aid civilian ship and plane navigation and to swiftly survey such Earth resources as crops, timber and water; development of improved communications satellites; maintenance of routine round-the-clock global weather watches from space, producing highly accurate long-range forecasts.

Late 1970s: First flight of a six-man interplanetary spacecraft, circling Mars and returning to Earth in 600 days (a similar but shorter trip about Venus is also possible); orbiting of giant astronomical telescopes above the Earth's obscuring atmosphere where they will be able to peer much farther into the universe than ground-based instruments can; establishment of a semi-permanent base on the moon to permit months of geological exploration and testing of equipment for later use on more distant planets.

Mid-1980s: Landing of men on Mars for 10 to 20 days of exploration; this enterprise, costing between $40 billion and $100 billion, would demand much of the space agency's ingenuity and energy during the decade and a half after the lunar landing.

The 1990s: Launching of unmanned probes to study Jupiter, Saturn and perhaps other planets; longer-duration astronaut exploration of Mars; maintenance of a small American colony on the moon; manned flights around the planets Jupiter and Saturn.

Tough technical problems remain to be solved before these objectives can be achieved, of course. The reliable operating life of such equipment as radio transmitters, maneuvering rockets and myriad electronic parts must be extended from a few months to many years. Spacecraft structures must be strengthened to withstand the damaging effects of the high vacuum and great temperature variations in space. Astronauts must learn to endure the psychological stresses of prolonged isolation in space. Effective antidotes to weightlessness, which may dangerously weaken the human body, must be found.

To propel spacecraft to the planets, nuclear rockets, producing twice the power of conventional chemically fueled engines, must be developed. Long-lasting, highly efficient sources of electrical power must be devised to operate spacecraft equipment for years and permit constant communications across millions of miles of space.

But money will be the major obstacle. United States space spending, now about $5 billion annually, must rise substantially in the years ahead if important parts of the rough timetable are to be accomplished. Some National Aeronautics and Space Administration officials say a yearly budget of $6 billion to $7 billion would be

89

sufficient to finance the Mars landing and most other tasks. Others contend a fixed portion of the gross national product, perhaps 1%, should be alloted to space; that would presumably mean a gradual climb in spending to $10 billion and beyond (GNP in 1966 was at an annual rate of $745 billion).

At any rate, most space specialists are convinced that with sufficient funds the technical troubles can be resolved. Some worries, such as weightlessness, may even prove exaggerated. "I personally think we will find out that the environment of space is the easiest environment man has ever encountered, once you pay the price of admission," says Stark Draper, director of the Massachusetts Institute of Technology's Instrumentation Laboratory and one of the nation's leading aeronautical engineers.

Why the United States should be willing to pay "the price of admission" is sometimes asked by critics of space ventures. But proponents of an extensive space program find ample justification for the effort.

They say it will help man to expand his knowledge of his immediate surroundings in space, to determine whether life exists on other planets, to probe the origin of the solar system and perhaps ultimately to understand the physical forces that created distant stars and planets. Besides scientific gains, they add, there are also the practical benefits expected in such fields as weather forecasting and navigation, as well as in military applications. Nor, they say, can the adventure aspect be ignored; space exploration offers man a chance to satisfy his ceaseless yearning for high adventure.

National prestige—in particular, the space race with Russia—is also a driving force behind the United States space program. Soviet space intentions are a mystery. But Russia's launching of larger and larger satellites and development of more powerful rocket boosters probably mean its cosmonauts are also headed for the moon and planets, American experts figure. Other countries, however, are expected to stick to unmanned satellite endeavors, mainly for communications. None will attempt to put a man in space, it's reasoned, because of the great cost.

The most ambitious United States space endeavor in the years ahead will be the campaign to land men on neighboring Mars. Most experts estimate the task can be accomplished by 1985. The major uncertainty is whether man can withstand the physical effects and mental isolation of nearly two years of space travel. Once the Mars spaceship starts on its journey, quick recall will be impossible because incredible quantities of fuel would be needed to reverse its flight for sudden return to Earth.

As a preliminary to the landing mission, a manned spaceship probably will be dispatched to "fly by" Mars and return to Earth in the late 1970s. Using gravitational attraction to swing about the planet, this spaceship will be lighter and of simpler design than the landing craft itself. The fly-by's major aim would be to precede the Russians in manned interplanetary flight, but significant scientific data would also be obtained.

"You would get a large burst of information as you go by because of proximity to the planet. An (unmanned) probe could be dispatched to sample the environment of the planet and then be recaptured by the spacecraft," says E. Z. Grey, former director of NASA's advanced missions planning.

The major advance required for landing men on Mars is the development of nuclear rockets to replace less efficient conventional liquid-chemical rockets. Despite the difficulties of operating intensely hot and radioactive nuclear reactors in space, experts are confident of success in the next decade.

"We've proven the technology already," declares Harold Finger, one of NASA's leading nuclear rocket experts. A small, 5,000-megawatt nuclear rocket reactor already has been tested successfully on the ground. Now engineers want to build and fly a reactor 10 times more powerful for interplanetary travel.

The Mars spaceship would weigh at least two million pounds, dwarfing the 90,000-pound Apollo lunar spaceship. Five nuclear rockets, each capable of producing 200,000 pounds of thrust, would send the craft to Mars, slow it down for landing and then return it to Earth.

Without nuclear propulsion, the Mars spacecraft would have to weigh 12 million pounds or more, with propelling fuel accounting for most of the weight. Great quantities of liquid hydrogen and liquid oxygen must be burned in conventional rocket engines to produce the hot exhaust gases for the forward thrust. The more efficient nuclear engine slashes weight by using a single propelling gas, liquid hydrogen, and by using atomic fission to heat it to higher temperatures, which result in greater thrust.

The Mars crew probably will consist of six or more men, sufficient for companionship and rotation of duties during the long journey. The astronauts will be carefully tested for emotional stability and physical endurance, particularly by lengthy confinement in isolation chambers on Earth. One crew member will be a doctor.

Their spacecraft will contain improved "life support" systems to conserve precious water and oxygen. Each astronaut consumes about eight pounds of these commodities daily. While reuse is not required on the one-week lunar trip, it will be essential during the longer Martian voyage.

Oxygen will be removed from exhaled carbon dioxide in the cabin by filtering through membranes or by chemical processes. Sweat, urine and other waste water also will be collected and purified. Excess water not required for drinking will be separated into its constituents by electrolysis and the oxygen used to replenish the cabin atmosphere.

A critical problem will be removal of poisonous

gases, such as carbon monoxide or methane, which might accumulate in the cabin during the long trip. "The main problem is man himself; you name it and he probably gives it off," declares one expert. The noxious agents will be made to adhere to charcoal or burned for conversion into less harmful materials.

Because the huge Mars craft will be far too heavy for launching as one unit from Earth, four to six chemically fueled Saturn V rockets will transport its major components separately into orbit 250 to 300 miles above the Earth's surface; there they will be assembled for the main flight. These major components will be the ship's nuclear rockets; a spacecraft that will carry the astronauts into orbit about Mars; a small "Mars Excursion Module" (MEM) to enable three or four spacemen to land on the planet; and a re-entry unit to shield the astronauts from the Earth's hot atmosphere on their return. (The nuclear rockets will be fired only in space, so as to avoid the dangers of an explosion on Earth.)

The astronauts will use "space tugs," slow-moving craft, to help them position and assemble the units of their Mars craft. Battery-driven wrenches will enable them to complete the connections. Then the interplanetary flight will begin. Three nuclear rockets will be fired to free the spaceship from Earth's gravity and speed it toward Mars. Most of the way the craft will coast under the sun's gravitational pull. A special nuclear braking blast will be needed to slow it sufficiently to orbit about Mars.

94

The landing itself, patterned on the lunar touch-down, will last 10 to 20 days. The 80,000 to 100,000-pound Mars excursion vehicle will be detached from the larger orbiting Mars craft, avoiding the need to slow the entire spaceship down for landing. The MEM will be shaped somewhat like a winged plane to permit maneuvering through the Martian atmosphere. However, it will be equipped with rocket engines allowing it to land gently and later take off to rejoin the mother ship for the trip home.

Re-entry into the Earth's atmosphere will be more difficult and dangerous for the Martian explorers than their lunar predecessors. After jettisoning its nuclear engines in space, the Mars craft will come hurtling into the atmosphere at 34,000 miles or more an hour, well above the moon-return speed of 25,000 m.p.h. Thicker heat shields as well as retro-rockets will be needed to slow its approach to Earth.

Long before the Mars mission, of course, United States astronauts presumably will have landed on the moon. Astronauts will spend only a few hours exploring the lunar landscape on the initial series of four moon missions planned under the Apollo program. But on these first missions the astronauts' craft will carry along digging tools, a rock-carrying container, cameras and a set of automated instruments to be set up on the moon, including a seismometer to check for moon quakes, a magnetometer to measure the moon's magnetic field and radiation detectors to determine the types and intensities of nuclear particles that bombard the moon. A tiny atomic generator will provide power for up to a year's operation of the instruments, long after the astronauts' departure.

On each trip the first Apollo explorers will carry back 80 pounds of surface material for laboratory analysis on Earth; the findings could help unravel uncertainties about the origin, evolution and chemical composition of the moon.

The next major advance in lunar exploration is expected in the early 1970s. A cargo-carrying version of the Apollo spacecraft will transport 2,500 pounds of supplies and equipment to the moon, sustaining astronauts for two weeks. A half-ton vehicle resembling a motorized golf cart will enable them to travel as far as five miles from their landing site.

On these excursions the astronauts would set up a network of automated scientific stations to supply prolonged and precise measurements of the moon, as well as astronomical observations of the stars. "A 12-inch space telescope on the moon will give you better results than Palomar's 200-inch instrument," predicts Jack Wild, director of advanced space programs for Westinghouse Electric Corporation, which is developing the stations for NASA.

The moon's stability and absence of atmosphere make it an ideal stellar observatory. The prime problem is fashioning delicate telescope mirrors that will not lose their shape in the weak lunar gravitational field or fracture under the stress of 500-degree fluctuations in temperature.

Later, space experts foresee establishment of a semipermanent lunar base, housing a dozen men who would rotate home at six-month intervals. Six men might share dome-shaped living quarters, insulated against the torrid lunar day and frigid night and shielded to withstand bombardment from high-intensity solar radiation. A 100-kilowatt nuclear reactor, similar to power plants used at remote Arctic bases, would furnish electricity for heat, light and communications.

A larger roving vehicle would enable the astronauts to range across 12,000 square miles of the lunar surface. Ultimately a flying craft would extend the exploration area to 25,000 square miles.

"A major problem is making equipment capable of operation in the lunar environment. The high vacuum is most difficult, leading to adhesion (of materials)," explains Rodney Johnson, a General Electric Company lunar expert.

Four flights a year of the Saturn V rocket would be needed to carry supplies and rotate the astronauts. The cost of establishing the base probably would range from $2 billion to $4 billion. Sizable additional outlays would be needed for its operation.

By the 1980s, barring insuperable obstacles, an 18- to 24-man lunar base might be established. By the turn of the century, some enthusiastic spacemen foresee a 50- to 100-man lunar colony.

While lunar exploration moves forward, extensive man-in-space operations will be conducted closer to home in orbit about the earth. The objectives will be preparation for interplanetary flight; medical evaluation of astronauts under space stresses; and testing of equipment to be used in weather, communications and other unmanned satellites. A starting step may come by 1970 with prolonged orbital journeys of the three-man Apollo spacecraft. Though the lunar craft is designed to stay aloft for only two weeks, the time could be extended to 45 days by adding extra power, oxygen and other supplies.

Spacemen might then attempt development of a six-man space station to remain in Earth orbit for a year. Such a station, measuring 22 feet in diameter and affording 15 times the living space of the Apollo craft, could serve as the crew quarters on a later flight to Mars. "We'd like to provide around-the-clock manning of several scientific disciplines, requiring communications specialists, meteorologists and astronomers," says John Disher, a NASA manned flight specialist.

The major aim of such lengthy flights will be to determine the physical effects and potential dangers of prolonged weightlessness. It's known the astronauts can safely endure two weeks' exposure with only minor transient side-effects, primarily the "pooling" of blood in the lower legs. But a 600-day mission to Mars could pose far greater hazards. Without the stress of gravity, bones lose strength-giving minerals and muscles atrophy. With lessened blood-pumping demands, blood volume decreases and veins distend. Medical men fear the heart will be unable to supply the body with enough blood when gravitational pressures are suddenly re-encountered.

To guard against this danger, "artificial gravity" will have to be created aboard spacecraft during long-duration flights, most space experts say. This would be achieved by substituting the whirling stresses of centrifugal force for the gravitational pull felt on Earth.

One approach, to be tested in the orbital space station, will be to install a centrifuge aboard the spacecraft. Each astronaut will crawl into the machine for a few hours a day to counteract the weakening effect of weightlessness. Some planners contend a more satisfactory solution, supplying constant artificial gravity, would be to rotate the entire spacecraft like a cartwheel as it travels through space. This would have to be done in a way that would keep the astronauts from rattling around perilously in their spacecraft or from losing command of their senses.

Along with medical experiments, the orbiting space station will serve as a platform for astronomical observations and other scientific studies. Space planners foresee operation of a 100-inch telescope by the late

1970s; its development would cost $1 billion. The instrument will be remotely controlled to avoid human interference with its delicate aiming equilibrium. But spacemen would be able to make simple repairs and carry stellar photographs back to Earth.

Orbital laboratories also will deploy huge 1,000-foot-long radio-telescope antennae to record stellar emanations that are absorbed by the Earth's atmosphere. "Of all the sciences likely to benefit, the greatest gainer will be astronomy," says one authority. "Once you are above the blanket of the atmosphere, a new world opens."

Late in this century a supersized space station may be lofted into Earth orbit. It will house two dozen astronauts and operate for five years. The Saturn V moon rocket, being developed for the lunar landing program, can lift 280,000 pounds and is powerful enough for this launching assignment. The crew of such a giant space station could repair unmanned communications and weather satellites, launch small craft that could rescue astronauts stranded in space and make scientific measurements of the Earth and its atmosphere.

Exploration of the solar system also will be conducted by costly and complex unmanned spacecraft in coming decades. The major objective will be to land automated life-detection instruments on Mars and perhaps later Venus, which some scientists think may be equally hospitable to life. By 1973, it's hoped, a 22,000-

pound spacecraft known as Voyager will set out on the search. The spacecraft will be carefully sterilized to avoid exporting contaminating microbes from Earth to Mars.

After the nine-month flight to Mars, Voyager will orbit the planet, measuring the size and number of micrometeorites and the strength and frequency of solar flares; it also will beam back live television pictures. Then a several-hundred-pound landing capsule will be dispatched to the planet's surface.

There the capsule's "automated biological laboratory" will begin its life-detection duties. Martian material will be dunked in a broth that contains radioactive tracers and nutrients known to speed the growth of Earthly bacteria. If reproduction occurs, the rising radiation given off by Martian microorganisms will send a telltale signal to Earth. Chemical analysis of Martian molecules will look for enzymes, the chemical catalysts that play a crucial part in most Earthly living processes. Optical studies, conparing light refraction patterns, will show whether Martian material resembles Earthly compounds.

The spaceships developed for Mars and Venus exploration will serve as building blocks for later, more ambitious missions to distant planets. As Mr. von Braun puts it: "There's a great deal of commonality of equipment—TV, sensors, power and telemetry. But the external spacecraft configuration may look quite different

101

beyond Mars. There would be no solar cells (because of the difficulty of deriving electrical power from the far distant sun) and maybe a bigger antenna dish (for improved communications)."

Jupiter, with its mysterious red spots and violent radio storms, is considered a tantalizing target. Scientists also would like to send unmanned satellites to Mercury, Saturn and the asteroid belts that are believed to be fragments of a primeval planet. Rendezvous with a comet may tell astronomers much about the composition and origin of these periodic intruders from outer space.

In coming decades, satellites will do more and more to help man live, work and learn on Earth. Besides communications satellites, there will be improved weather satellites to help meteorologists extend the accuracy of their current 24- and 48-hour forecasts to as long as two weeks. Infrared heat-sensing instruments will provide pictures of the Earth's cloud cover in the dark, complementing photos taken in daylight. A network of instrument-equipped balloons, floating above the ocean expanses, will beam temperature, humidity, density and wind-speed measurements to weather satellites passing overhead.

Ultimately a constant weather watch will be provided by four high-altitude meteorological satellites orbiting 22,300 miles above the Earth's surface. These satellites, revolving at the same rate as the Earth, will photograph the entire globe every 20 minutes. (Earlier weather satellite systems will furnish such global coverage only once a day.) As a result, meteorologists will be able to detect immediately the embryonic development of storms and warn people well in advance of weather dangers.

Civilian navigation and traffic-control satellites will guide planes and help them land at crowded terminals. Ships also will use the system. A three-satellite system will serve 90% of the world. These satellites, each beaming out a steady radio signal, will enable aircraft and ships to determine their positions within about 1.5 miles.

Orbiting satellites also will be used to help make surface maps, detect forest fires, measure crop yields and survey certain other natural resources on Earth. Such "sensing" satellites will be equipped with cameras, infrared heat detectors and other instruments. "A well-organized system could be operating by the mid-1970s," predicts Peter Badgley, a NASA expert. Among the predicted annual economies: $3 million for timber surveys and $32 million for forest fire prevention.

Besides savings, speed will be an advantage. Oceanographic vessels take years to survey a single sea; one satellite could do important elements of the job in only days. It would receive and record measurements of ocean depths, currents and the like that are broadcast by instrumented buoys floating in the water.

Among other possible Earth-satellite services suggested by space experts: Population estimates could be made from photographs of cities and rural regions; for animal migration studies, tiny radio transmitters could be attached to deer and other species to broadcast their wanderings to satellites overhead.

—JONATHAN SPIVAK

The Cities:

Our Crowded Society

If you don't like urban life, start running.

Houses and concrete and businesses and schools will spill over more of the countryside in coming decades. In the central sections of cities buildings will soar higher and the atmosphere will grow still more impersonal. The noise level will climb as new types of short-haul intercity aircraft capable of operating from tiny downtown landing strips begin adding their jet roar to the present din.

But the citified society of the future may not be quite as grim as some pessimists would have you believe. Though urban "sprawl" is expected to continue, most planners are confident their campaigns for land-use projects that leave green spaces for recreation will start to pay off soon. Transit experts predict that dramatic progress in their field will ease commuting for people who work in the central city but live in new suburbs 100 miles or more distant; "air-cushion" vehicles that shoot through tubes at speeds up to 600 miles an hour or more are one of the proposed new modes of commuter transportation.

In the core areas of cities, slums will largely disappear, though some aging, ill-planned suburban subdivisions will take on a slum-like aspect. The crime rate will drop in cities, partly because television and other surveillance devices will improve police efficiency. Racial tensions also will decline sharply, in the view of some sociologists.

Another urban problem, downtown congestion, will be alleviated by turning many crowded streets into pedestrian malls and by barring private cars from some areas. Restrictions on the use of autos—or at least on those powered by internal-combustion engines—may also help combat air pollution. And some researchers go so far as to predict that a number of urban communities will solve the pollution problem completely by enveloping themselves in vast air-conditioned plastic canopies where residents will breathe filtered air—and bask in an ideal climate year round.

Planners balk at setting precise timetables for many of the changes they foresee in urban areas between now and the year 2000. True, marvels like domed cities or jet-speed commuting face enough technological and other problems so their advent probably can be safely assigned to the closing years of the century, if then.

But in some fields, such as pollution and land-use planning, the pace of change hinges to a considerable extent on the ability of local and regional administrative units to cooperate. Otherwise, confused, overlapping jurisdictions will frustrate efforts to carry out rational solutions to the problems of growing urban areas. With a few exceptions, urban planners note, past attempts to achieve metropolitan and regional cooperation have met dogged resistance, and the experts can't predict when problems will become serious enough to break down such opposition.

The role of the Federal Government is another imponderable in the future of cities. Rightly or wrongly, cities look to Washington for massive help in attacking slums and crime and in improving mass transit. So the rate of progress in these fields will depend to a high degree on the money and impetus from Washington— which, in turn, may depend on how preoccupied the United States remains with overseas problems, such as Vietnam.

Nevertheless, certain urban trends are clear. The most unmistakable one is that more and more people will live in urban areas.

At present some 70%—or 139 million—of the total United States population of 198 million are classed as city dwellers under Census Bureau standards. By 2000 a minimum of 83%—or 281 million—of a total population of 338 million are expected to be living in urban areas. Some analysts regard the 83% projection as far too low, contending the proportion of city residents will top 90% by the end of the century.

Experts agree that almost all these new urban dwell-

107

ers will settle in the suburbs, at least through the next couple of decades or so. Typically, Robert C. Wood, Undersecretary of the Department of Housing and Urban Development, says that what he terms the "spread city of the 1940s-60s era" will remain "the dominant form for some time to come."

Urban and suburban sprawl will produce immense metropolitan areas—"megalopolises"—in some parts of the United States. By 2000, experts say, unbroken stretches of urban civilization will run from just above Boston to below Washington, D.C., some 450 miles; from Chicago to Detroit, over 250 miles; from Cleveland to Buffalo; and from Santa Barbara (100 miles north of Los Angeles) to the Mexican border.

Many authorities think that central cities, most of which have lost population in recent decades, eventually will have a new surge of growth. The suburbs will continue to grow, too, but, says William L. C. Wheaton, a professor of planning at the University of California, "by the 1990s cities will be exciting enough to be drawing people back in, causing many with homes in the country to take up apartments in the city as well."

Metropolitan areas abroad as well as those in the United States are expected to grow rapidly, and in some poorer parts of the world in Asia, the Mideast and Africa the expanding throngs of urban dwellers may pose almost insuperable problems. It is difficult to envision how the Indian city of Calcutta, for example,

will be able to cope with the population of 30 million—
five times the present total—that is forecast for it by
2000; already 600,000 residents of Calcutta are said to
be homeless squatters.

But in the United States urban planners hope they
can shape growth so tomorrow's vast metropolises will
be manageable by governments and hospitable to residents.

One of the planners' key aims, the preservation of
open spaces in or near cities, takes on new urgency
every day. It's estimated that well under 5% of the
United States land area is now urbanized, but vacant
acreage in urban areas is being gobbled up. Once a
chunk of landscape that would be ideal for a park is
blanketed with split-levels, the return of the area to
open land may be too costly. Besides destroying recreational areas, formless urban growth results in incon-
venience for residents and increases the cost of providing services such as garbage collection and police protection, according to urban authorities.

At present planning agencies can generally do little
more than recommend the directions in which metropolitan areas should grow, but even with this limited
function they are beginning to make headway. Consider the efforts of the Maryland-National Capital Park
Planning Commission, which consists of representatives
of two Maryland counties, Montgomery and Prince
Georges, that are suburbs of Washington.

The commission's assignment is to guide the municipalities in the counties so that their housing, business and recreational development will fit into an overall scheme. The commission says that so far the municipalities have largely adhered to its plan.

This plan calls for development to be channeled along six "corridors" radiating 40 to 50 miles out from Washington. Each corridor contains four or five cities, some new, some well established. Parkways or strips of greenery will prevent cities in the same corridor from blending into each other, while the wedges of open space between the corridors will provide close-in recreational areas for all. The plan creates the dense lines of development needed for low-cost mass transit, planners note. It also preserves physically separate towns, which sociologists say creates a sense of identity that stimulates civic pride and makes for safer, more attractive communities.

The "New Town" movement offers another approach to the problem of urban sprawl. It envisions the creation in open countryside of new communities that would have their own employment opportunities, stores and recreational facilities, so residents would not have to travel long distances daily.

The New Town idea is not new. One of the earliest of these self-contained communities was the "garden city" of Letchworth in England, built some 60 years ago on a site 35 miles north of London. Scores of other New Towns have since sprung up in England, the Scandinavian lands and other European nations on both sides of the Iron Curtain.

New Towns have been much slower to catch on in the United States. One reason is a lack of assistance by government agencies. In Europe government land-condemnation powers and financial backing have smoothed the way for many New Town projects. But two private American developers recently embarked on New Town ventures on their own.

Both these New Towns are near Washington, D.C. One is the work of a Baltimore mortgage banker named James W. Rouse. A firm he heads, the Rouse Company, is beginning construction of the New Town of Columbia on a 25-square-mile tract of Maryland countryside between Washington and Baltimore. Columbia is supposed to house some 125,000 people by 1980, along with enough offices, industries and stores to employ almost all the breadwinners among the residents.

The other United States New Town, considerably further along than Columbia, is the work of New York real estate investor Robert E. Simon and his Simon Enterprises Incorporated. This town is Reston, Virginia, located on 11 square miles 17 miles northwest of Washington and planned as a city of 75,000 eventually.

Some 1,500 people moved into the first section of Reston to be completed, and their surroundings arouse envy in most visitors. Townhouses, detached single-

111

family homes and high-rise apartments blend attractively. They overlook a 33-acre artificial lake, from which noisy motors and all boats over 18 feet are banned. Pleasant paths crisscross the community, inviting strollers and liberating mothers from endless chauffeuring. A supermarket and other shops are handy. Parking and access roads are all in the rear of houses, and industrial enterprises are just over the hill.

But, in common with many European New Towns, Reston is encountering difficulty in becoming a truly self-contained community. It has managed to attract a half-dozen research centers, and the United States Geological Survey plans to locate its offices there. But Mr. Simon says that only 25% of Reston's jobholders actually work in Reston, and he concedes he is not as hopeful as he once was that this proportion will swell to 50% or more. Moreover, only about 25% of the people presently working in Reston live in the town. Thus, the Reston project isn't fulfilling one of its primary goals—the creation of a community where most people live close to their work.

"We're just too mobile for our cities to be self-contained," says HUD's Mr. Wood. Nevertheless, he sees the New Towns as far superior to uncontrolled urban expansion and predicts that they will proliferate. Spurring the trend, in his view, will be the entry of more large companies into the community-building field; General Electric Company, for one, has established a Community Systems Development Division and announced its intention to become a city-builder. Some Federal officials also believe that in time private builders of New Towns will get financing aid from Washington and land-condemnation help from local governments.

The expectation that governments will encourage the construction of New Towns is based on the assumption that the need for some sort of planning to insure ordered urban growth eventually will be recognized by almost everyone. As Edward J. Logue, boss of Boston's redevelopment agency, puts it: "By the year 2000 some kind of green belt or open space policy will be effectively in force as the discovery is more generally made that sprawl just doesn't make sense."

But not all forecasters are this optimistic. Daniel Bell, a Columbia University professor of sociology and chairman of the Commission on the Year 2000, which was established in 1965 by the American Academy of Arts and Sciences to examine a variety of future problems, fears many large metropolitan areas won't take the ambitious planning measures needed to make their growth rational. Consequently, he expects smaller cities, particularly well-situated ones in the 50,000 to 100,000 category, to grow fastest in the future, simply because they will be more livable and therefore more attractive to job-generating industries.

Programs for rebuilding the old central cities of metropolitan areas could well prove easier to carry out

113

than plans to guide suburban growth. One reason is that in core-area planning only one local government is involved, eliminating the need to reconcile the views of several jurisdictions.

Strong political pressures also are likely to speed the renaissance of metropolitan cores. Says Edward C. Banfield, professor of government at Harvard: "There's too much political power in our central cities for the Federal Government to let the cities go under and too much power in central business districts for central cities to let their downtowns go under."

As a result of such factors, authorities expect most city centers to undergo drastic transformations in the years ahead. Some aspects of these transformations will have their detractors. A number of critics complain, for example, that rebuilding programs break up close-knit neighborhoods. But the majority of urban planners obviously think the benefits far outweigh the drawbacks.

Rebutting the criticism of the disruption of old neighborhoods, they note that many of these are Negro ghettos. Dispersion of the residents into formerly all-white neighborhoods, while it may produce frictions initially, could contribute significantly to improved race relations in the long run. "By 2000 we'll be wondering what all the shouting was about," says sociologist Daniel P. Moynihan, director of the Joint Center for Urban

114

Studies at Massachusetts Institute of Technology and Harvard.

Some of the decaying structures due for destruction will be replaced by vertical cities within the city. These immense complexes may achieve heights of 200 or more stories, compared with 102 for the Empire State Building. They will contain apartments for tens of thousands of families, along with offices, shops and recreational areas. In theory, residents would hardly ever have to step outside.

Century City in Los Angeles is considered a forerunner of the city-within-a-city of the future. Located on a former movie lot, it now boasts two major office buildings, a hotel, two luxury apartment towers and a shopping center. Century City will accommodate some 12,000 residents and provide 20,000 jobs by the time all segments are completed in the late 1970s.

The creation of pedestrian malls to make downtown areas more pleasant aroused wide interest several years ago, and a handful of cities tried them out. Some merchants objected, however; they feared loss of business if customers couldn't draw up at the front door in their cars. Some cities, including Toledo and Springfield, Oregon, laid out malls, then had second thoughts and turned the streets over to auto traffic again.

But now the mall concept is reviving as city planners convince the critics that malls can unclog downtown

115

streets and make them more attractive places to shop and work. Los Angeles, Detroit, Houston, Minneapolis, Cincinnati, Elizabeth (New Jersey) and Philadelphia are either planning pedestrian malls or already building them.

Philadelphia will have a particularly extensive and elaborate pedestrian mall. Scheduled for completion in 1975, it will run for 10 blocks in the heart of the city. Edmund Norwood Bacon, Philadelphia's top city planner, says the mall will have benches, fountains, sculpture and plantings. Within 10 years, the city also hopes to install a moving belt or "carveyor"—individual seats on a belt—to carry people along at least part of the mall, according to Mr. Bacon. Transit lines and delivery vehicles will travel on a level beneath the mall—an idea a number of other cities may copy by simply building malls over existing streets.

Still another feature of the Philadelphia mall—a glass roof to protect pedestrians from the elements—foreshadows the much more ambitious efforts to build domed communities.

Eugene B. Konecci, a staff member of a Presidential space advisory panel whose studies of habitations for men in the hostile environment of space are closely related to research on domed communities on Earth, is one of several authorities who expect such communities to begin appearing by the year 2000. Domes would win acceptance fastest in areas of severe air pollution or where year-round climate control is considered important, he suggests. Initially, private enterprise probably would provide the impetus, perhaps by building clear plastic canopies over swimming pools and other recreational facilities in apartment complexes.

General Electric's TEMPO Division, whose staff members devote their days to thinking about the future, agrees that domes may be feasible. A TEMPO report notes that technologists like Buckminster Fuller claim they can construct a plastic canopy one mile high and two miles in diameter for about $200 million. TEMPO doesn't view such an outlay as prohibitive; moreover, it says technological advances probably will lower the cost of domes.

Greatly improved mass transit will be essential to link tomorrow's central cities and the ever more distant fringes of metropolitan areas, urban planners stress. Though many jobs will move to the suburbs along with families, armies of commuters will still pour into the metropolitan cores daily. As these trips become longer and expressway traffic becomes more congested, swift new transit will be the only recourse.

How quickly transit needs are met is particularly dependent on developments in the political field. In major metropolitan areas transit lines must cross municipal, county and even state lines, making cooperation among several governmental units vital. The trials faced by the San Francisco area in its efforts to build a new $1

117

billion-plus rapid transit system illustrate some of the problems; routes have had to be redrawn time after time in keeping with the demands of the communities the system will serve.

Though San Francisco is managing with little help from Washington, experts think many metropolitan areas will be unable to create new transit systems without Federal funds.

Some methods for improving transit—such as the reservation of expressway lanes for the exclusive use of buses—are relatively simple. But in most places the provision of adequate transit service will be an enormously expensive undertaking, and local governments and private firms are likely to lack the resources to tackle it.

Already Washington is taking on some responsibilities in transit. Under a 1964 law the Government can offer communities loans or grants to improve mass transit, plus aid for transit research. The Federally supported project to run 110-mile-per-hour trains between New York and Washington starting in 1967 is part of a broad program of Federal research into high-speed ground transportation that could eventually pay off in better mass transit systems.

Transit specialists are exploring many ideas. New or expanded subway systems will serve at least as short-term solutions to transit problems in some cities. Monorail is still considered a good possibility for single-leg transit service, such as the new monorail line linking

118

Tokyo's airport and downtown. But difficulties with switching may rule out monorail for complex systems.

Far swifter than subway trains or monorail, however, would be the 600-mile-an-hour air-cushion vehicles now under development. Laboratory models of such vehicles have been built at the University of Manchester in Britain and at MIT. Garrett Corporation, a Los Angeles subsidiary of Signal Oil Company that makes components for space vehicles and electric power systems, has a Federal contract to study the feasibility of the concept.

Electromagnetic energy from a power source embedded in a concrete roadbed would pull the wheel-less vehicles along. When at rest or slowing down they would settle onto the roadbed, but at other times they would travel inches above the surface. They would blast jets of air against the walls of the tube enclosing the system in order to keep centered over the roadbed and on course. The tube would muffle noise from the vehicles that might otherwise disturb areas along the right-of-way.

The high-speed air-cushion vehicles, which researchers think are 20 to 30 years off, could supplement air transport on heavily traveled intercity routes. But they would also be suitable for the long-distance commutes of the future.

A West Coast executive could live on a hilltop overlooking the Pacific Ocean at Carmel, California, for example, and commute the 300 miles to Los Angeles with ease. He might board his reserved-seat air-cushion coach at Carmel at 8:15 a.m. It would lift off the road-bed, whirl around an acceleration loop and plunge into the main tube running from Seattle to San Diego. Little more than half an hour later the car would peel off onto the deceleration loop in downtown Los Angeles. By 9 a.m. the executive would be at his desk.

—MITCHELL GORDON

Automobiles:

Cleaner and Safer

As far as auto makers are concerned, today's car is nearly perfect. In their view, its gas-fueled power plant far surpasses any alternative in sight, and no reasonable man could fault such features as automatic transmission, power steering and brakes, air conditioning and stereo-tape players. Thus, except for changes in looks, it would seem the future should bring only evolutionary refinements.

But even Detroit doesn't expect things to work out this way. It is bracing for a prolonged period of change, not so much to satisfy its customers as to assuage its critics. For the remarkable success of this century's automotive revolution is beginning to boomerang.

More than 70 million cars now travel United States streets and highways. They give Americans untold convenience and pleasure, and the industry that manufactures them serves as one of the main props of the economy. But Detroit's critics insist the number of autos has reached a point where they also give rise to serious problems—traffic jams, air pollution, rising accident

121

deaths and defacement of cities by freeways. And more and more often the critics' complaints are winning a sympathetic hearing in Washington and in local and state governments.

"We've noticed in recent years that the automobile is getting singled out for the ills of our congested society," grumbles one auto executive. "Many planners think the auto is the cause of all troubles."

Auto makers see the outline of the future in laws calling for Federal safety standards and anti-smog devices for new cars. Says Harry Chesebrough, vice president in charge of Chrysler Corporation's product planning and development activities: "The economic, political and social effects of the automobile have been so profound that increasingly the auto will be shaped and, to some extent, controlled by the very forces it has created."

The auto industry, instead of resisting the new pressures from outsiders the way it once fought demands for safety innovations, now is trying hard to meet complaints. Its researchers are looking into design changes far beyond anything required by the specifications of existing or anticipated laws. Their efforts, which are supplemented by important work going on outside the auto industry, are expected to bring such developments as these:

● Vast communications networks between cars and computerized traffic control stations, possibly employing information collected by Earth-orbiting satellites or aerial surveillance.

● Introduction of automatic steering, braking and acceleration, governed by "eyes" in the front of the car or by sensing devices that pick up information from the roadbed.

● A limited revival of electric cars and introduction of turbine engines as part of the battle to reduce air pollution.

High costs, technology gaps and other problems will bar quick arrival of any of these developments. But there are knowledgeable men in Detroit and elsewhere who predict that electric propulsion, automatic governing devices and traffic-control stations linked to cars will be in limited use as early as 1975.

Even if advances such as these work out, the role of the auto seems certain to be circumscribed in some crowded smog-ridden metropolitan areas in coming decades. In a few cities suggestions have been made to limit access by autos to central sections by such devices as charging a high fee for use of the streets. Many metropolitan areas are developing plans to revitalize their mass transit systems after years of inattention; such plans usually include arrangements for parking cars on the periphery of cities and using transit for travel in the congested cores.

But auto makers have no fears that cars will be eclipsed. Declares Henry Ford II, chairman of Ford

123

Motor Company and grandson of the industry pioneer: "There has been a lot of talk for a long time about people tubes, monorails and other developments that will supposedly make the automobile obsolete. The fact is, however, that for most travel purposes, no vehicles have yet been developed or are even in prospect that equal the automobile for speed, comfort, convenience, privacy, economy and other qualities that people value."

Auto men, in fact, expect more rather than fewer cars per capita in the United States in the future. They see as commonplace the three-car family—or, as one Detroiter puts it, "more cars than kids." About 20% of the nation's families already own more than one car. By 1985 the proportion is likely to reach 40%. By the year 2000, auto makers say, there may be as many as 200 million cars in the United States—nearly three times today's total and almost equivalent to one car for each adult. Americans are expected to be buying at least 22 million new cars and maybe as many as 25 million a year by 2000, compared with the mid-1960s annual rate of around 9 million.

The high rate of car ownership will result both from rising affluence and from the fact that most of the nation's population growth will continue to be concentrated in the suburbs, where cars are essential. Since 1950, a Ford economist notes, all United States population growth has come in the suburbs, and during this period the number of cars in the United States has doubled. "Cars made the suburbs possible," comments the economist.

Now, he adds, suburbs are "creating pressure not just for one car but for multiple ownership." Factories, stores and offices as well as housing have sprung up in the suburbs, and this has led to a tremendous increase in travel between various suburban points. For such trips, efficient mass transit service is generally lacking, and it probably will continue to be unavailable, since transit planners are focusing mainly on high-volume runs between the outskirts and the cores of metropolitan areas.

"The type of trips for which the auto is the rational solution is growing fantastically," says Irving Rubin, director of Detroit's regional transportation and land use study.

The proliferation of families with more than one car is likely to be spurred further by the trend to special-purpose vehicles. The family sedan already has had to share its market with the station wagon and the new sporty cars like the Mustang, and other new types of vehicles are now envisioned.

A little "shopper," perhaps electric powered and probably smaller than today's compact, is a strong possibility; it might have three wheels, seats for just two people and a door that opens from the front. A family might also have a full-sized "cruiser" for between-cities travel, possibly with automatic controls. Specialized recreation vehicles, such as weekend campers or combination carboats with wheels that retract on entering the water, may also come into wide use.

To make road room for all these cars, the Federally supported highway-building program obviously will have to continue beyond the present mid-1970s completion target. But more room will be needed for cars off the highway, too.

"The first floor of future homes will be turned over to cars," forecasts one General Motors Corporation official. "That's right—five-car garages." Some auto men think eventually many cities will require that new buildings in central areas have parking structures alongside or parking basements.

Disposing of old cars will also pose a massive problem. "People are getting rid of cars faster, even though cars are built to last longer," says a Ford marketing analyst. "It's a by-product of our affluent society."

Americans currently are junking six million cars a year. The total is expected to double by 1985 and perhaps triple by 2000. Some old cars are melted down for scrap, but this makes only a tiny dent in the mounting heaps of junked cars that are eyesores to Lady Bird Johnson and others eager to beautify the United States. The problem with melting down cars, says a GM researcher, is that "you end up with a mixture that is not too valuable." Some authorities predict auto buyers eventually will be charged extra—say, $25 a car—to cover the cost of a national car-burying program, run either by private industry or the Federal Government.

There's no consensus in Detroit on what tomorrow's car will look like. But many stylists agree with the view of James Roche, GM president, that "aerodynamics will play an increasing part in the automotive design." Aside from any aesthetic considerations, exteriors with sleeker lines and fewer bulges would improve fuel economy and cut wind noise, stylists say.

With rapidly improving air-conditioning, some designers suggest that wind noise could be eliminated completely by sealing all the windows. But this would run into the problems of claustrophobia and paying tolls when the windows won't open.

Auto interiors may get more airplane-like, too, especially the control mechanisms. Steering wheels have been replaced in some test cars with a pair of smaller wheels, one for each hand. GM has experimented with a "uni-control" stick that causes the car to accelerate when pushed forward, brake when pulled back and turn when moved from side to side; a red button on top toots the horn. Ease of handling is the goal of such changes.

Whether these control innovations will soon—or ever —reach commercial production is uncertain. One of the biggest obstacles to radically different controls is the older driver's instinctive reactions in an emergency;

127

GM, for example, worries about which way a driver would move the uni-control stick in a sudden crisis. Whatever the final decisions on new controls, they would appear first as optional equipment.

Safety will be the aim of many innovations. Michael Ference Jr., Ford vice president for scientific research, predicts standard equipment someday will include instrument warning lights to alert drivers to such dangers as doors that are ajar or tires that are low on air; some Ford models already have warning-light systems. Other Ford officials say cars will have better rearview devices —perhaps periscopes or small closed-circuit television systems instead of mirrors.

The stress on safety already has prompted Ford to start work on front-ends designed to crumple in such a way as to ease the impact of a crash. Other safety possibilities are roof-mounted stop signals for better visibility (some French-made Citroens already have these) and fixed front seats, with adjustments for individual drivers made by changing the position of the pedals and steering column rather than by sliding the seat back and forth. Designers agree that they could build a safer car if they could make the front seat rigid.

Cars will become more comfortable as well as safer, though experts say care must be taken not to make the driver so relaxed he dozes off. In the big cruiser cars swivel chairs may replace the front passenger seat and the back seat bench, says Mr. Chesebrough of Chrysler.

In an experimental station wagon built by Ford, the middle seat bench is replaced by a sofa that curves around the side behind the driver. Arjay Miller, president of Ford, says that by the early 1970s cars will have "contour seats" that will adjust automatically to the dimensions of each occupant.

The traffic control systems that the experts are counting on to make congestion bearable already are operating on a limited basis in some cities. The systems use monitoring devices to determine the density and speed of traffic. These are hooked up to computers that analyze this information and automatically change traffic light timing or the direction of traffic in freeway lanes so as to speed the flow of cars.

Such electronic networks are certain to become more widespread and more elaborate. One added wrinkle may be railroad-type barrier gates at the entrance ramps to freeways to keep cars out when the road is overloaded and let them in when traffic lightens—a development that might have its infuriating aspects for a motorist waiting in line to enter a freeway but that would at least keep him from getting caught in a hopeless jam.

Recently the Federal Government has started to pay for computers and related equipment under the highway program. Before long, says an official of the Bureau of Public Roads, "you'll see more emphasis on computers than concrete."

129

Television surveillance of traffic by the police also will grow. An experimental system using 14 TV cameras already is in operation on a three-mile stretch of Detroit's John Lodge Freeway. From television observation, controllers discovered that obstructions in just one of the three north- or south-bound lanes could slow traffic so much that capacity in one direction was cut in half. By using illuminated signs suspended from overpasses to divert traffic to open lanes the instant they spot an accident or breakdown, the controllers can keep the flow of cars much closer to normal.

But eventually traffic will reach the point where such systems will be inadequate. The next step, researchers figure, will be the networks linking individual cars with traffic control centers. Via radio, drivers will get instructions on less congested alternate routes and warnings about traffic hazards or obstructions ahead.

Henry Ford is enthusiastic about the potential of this type of traffic control. "In the future," he has said, "we foresee the possible development of a nationwide traffic control system based on Earth survey satellites or aerial reconnaissance linked by computer to urban traffic control centers and finally to the stop light on the corner and even to the radio in your car. As fantastic as it may seem, we believe such a system will be technically feasible and economically sound."

Automatic control of cars is still further in the future, but it's nevertheless considered a good possibility for introduction before the end of this century. Although high costs will be a big problem, many auto researchers say it is technically feasible now to control the speed and steering of cars through the use of sensing devices that pick up signals from guidance wires embedded in a roadway or along its edge.

Such equipment could be used just for warnings; for example, it could trigger a buzzer when a car starts to swerve out of its lane. On a limited access highway, it could do much more, however. It could allow a driver to go from one city to another without touching the steering wheel or pressing the accelerator. The driver's role would be like that of the pilot of a plane flying with the controls on automatic pilot.

"The technology is here, but the economics are a problem," says Robert Weeks, a transportation specialist for General Electric Company. The principal outlay—for control equipment built into highways—would have to be borne by governments. But Mr. Weeks says the cost of control equipment for an individual car might still run as high as $500.

Cost is not the only hitch. Ways would have to be found to keep cars not equipped for automatic control off controlled-travel highways and to switch cars from automatic to more conventional operation once they leave the special highways. There is also a legal question: In case of an accident is the driver or the highway to blame?

Despite such problems, some transportation men expect that within 10 to 15 years Washington and the states will build experimental stretches of highways equipped for automatically controlled cars. As for fully automated major highways, Lowell Bridwell, Federal Highway Administrator, estimates that these are at least 25 years away.

Some traffic and auto researchers think a less complex form of automatic control might precede the construction of automated highways. It would result from the development of "seeing" devices attached to the car. These would eliminate the need for installing guidance equipment in the road.

"Proximity warning devices," which could become available within 10 years, could evolve into seeing devices capable of controlling a car. The warning devices would measure the distance between cars by sending out a light or sound beam and warn the driver if his car was approaching another car too fast. Besides improving highway safety, such devices would permit closer spacing of vehicles. Eventually, the information they gather could be translated into instructions for automatic steering, braking and acceleration equipment.

The revival of electric autos will almost certainly come along sooner than automatically controlled vehicles; it probably will start within the next decade. Electric-powered cars are nothing new, of course. In the early days of autos they were dominant. But since the 1920s Detroit has favored the gasoline-fueled piston engine as the most efficient, powerful and reliable means of propelling cars. And auto makers still maintain that no other type of propulsion now known—including batteries, fuel-cells or turbines—will ever outperform today's engines.

Yet within and without the auto industry, electric power is getting a second look. One reason is that battery and fuel-cell technology is advancing fast. But the rising clamor over air pollution is the chief motivating force.

Rightly or wrongly, cars are receiving most of the blame for smog. And even with anti-smog devices, which Federal law specifies for all new cars starting with 1968 models, plus various engine improvements in the works, Detroit knows of no way to eliminate completely the air-polluting hydrocarbon emissions of internal-combustion power plants. Moreover, researchers note, whatever reductions may be achieved in the emissions from individual cars are likely to be offset by the rising auto population.

The concern about air pollution, which already has led to suggestions for limiting car use in New York and Los Angeles, suddenly makes electric cars attractive again. They emit no pollutants.

But electric cars aren't practical with present batteries, auto makers say. The batteries are too bulky; in an experimental Corvair in which GM has tried sub-

133

stituting batteries for a gasoline engine, the batteries occupy most of the engine and luggage compartments. Another drawback is that most present batteries will propel a car less than 40 miles in city driving without being recharged—and they can't be recharged more than 100 times.

A flurry of research is under way in hope of overcoming these problems. Besides the auto makers, such firms as Westinghouse Electric Corporation, General Electric Company, General Dynamics Corporation and Union Carbide Corporation are engaged in the effort. Some companies involved remain highly skeptical about electric autos for the near future. GM, for example, sees almost no use of the cars before 1985, though Lawrence Hafstad, vice president in charge of GM's research laboratories, raises the possibility that air pollution could produce a real swing to electrics by 2000.

Ford expects electric-car technology to move along much faster. In October 1966 it announced what it called a "major breakthrough in battery research." It said it was developing a new sodium-sulphur battery that could propel a Falcon-sized car 82 miles in city traffic before needing a recharge and that could be recharged indefinitely.

Ford says it sees a market for electrics as small "subcompact" cars for town driving. In England, where gasoline costs twice as much as in the United States and thus the advantages of the gasoline engine over battery power are not quite so overwhelming, there already is such a market; some 50,000 electric milk trucks creep along the streets of London at top speed of 18 to 20 miles an hour. Ford plans tests of electrics using commercially available batteries in the United States and England in 1968. It promises commercial production in five to ten years.

Westinghouse rivals Ford's optimism. One of its transportation specialists, George Jernstedt, predicts there will be 100,000 battery-powered cars in the United States by 1975.

Though utility men exult at the thought of thousands of electric cars using current every night for recharging, one avenue of electric auto research holds no prospect of gain for them. This is the effort to perfect the fuel cell. Fuel cells, which produce electricity by combining chemicals, don't require recharging. It's simply necessary to replenish the supply of chemicals periodically. Some researchers suggest the ideal electric car would combine fuel cells and batteries, relying mainly on the fuel cells, but drawing on the batteries for extra power for acceleration.

Another combination possibility is a car powered by batteries and a conventional engine. Ford is working on such a car. It would run on batteries for city driving

135

and then switch to the gas engine when it hits open country, where pollution dangers are lower. This approach would overcome the lack of range and power that will make the kind of electrics presently envisioned unsuitable for high-speed, long-distance driving.

Short of going the electric-power route, some authorities think gas turbines probably offer the best hope for reducing auto-caused pollution. Today's reciprocating engine mixes air and gasoline in a carburetor and shoots the resulting mist into a cylinder. There it is compressed and ignited, and the explosion forces the piston down. The up-and-down motion of the pistons forces a crankshaft to turn and makes the car's wheels turn.

Turbines get the same results by compressing and heating air, then forcing the hot air through a turbine wheel that spins the car's drive shaft. One of the problems with turbines is that no one has yet found a material capable of taking the intense heat but cheap enough to use in auto engines. Another problem is that turbines gulp great quantities of fuel. Also, they are inefficient at low speeds.

"You step on the accelerator and nothing happens," says GM's Mr. Hafstad. "Then five or six seconds later the power comes on with a rush. This would make crossing a busy intersection a really sporting proposition."

But turbines produce fewer hydrocarbon emissions

than piston engines, and many auto men think this advantage will spur the industry to overcome turbines' technical snags. By 1985, declares Ford's Mr. Ference, "there will be a lot of gas turbines around."

—LAURENCE G. O'DONNELL

The Home:

Automated Living

Keeping house will be a breeze by the year 2000.

Sonic cleaning devices and air-filtering systems will banish dirt and just about eliminate dusting, scrubbing and vacuuming Combination freezer-microwave ovens will take care of the cooking automatically. Dishwashing will be a thing of the past, since disposable dishes will be made from powdered plastic for each meal by a machine in the kitchen. Permanent-press clothes will do away with ironing.

Such, at least, is domestic life at the end of this century as envisioned by researchers and designers at Philco-Ford Corporation, a subsidiary of Ford Motor Company. The sketch they draw of the future obviously will not materialize in every American home by 2000. But the technology to make Philco's vision a reality is available today, and experts outside Philco agree there will be steady progress toward homes that are nearly work-free.

The transformation of the interior of the home—which many authorities expect to be much more dramatic than the changes in the way homes look from the outside—will greatly expand the housewife's leisure time. And the home will be equipped with electronic marvels that will enable her to put her new freedom to good use.

Her morning coffee klatch, for example, could forsake gossip to watch a video tape of *King Lear* rented from the local library and displayed on a big three-dimensional television screen on the living-room wall. Perhaps joined by her husband, who will also have more leisure because of a shorter work week, she could spend a late-afternoon hour studying a programed course in small-boat handling and navigation piped into her house from a computer at an adult education center.

To men like Paul McCobb, a New York designer who helped Philco develop its plan for the home of the future, tomorrow's dwellings promise Americans a "great adventure" in living. Some people are a shade less optimistic, however.

It's true "the opportunities will be greater for self-fulfillment in community life, art, politics and education," says R. C. Sandin, a thoughtful Swede who is manager of industrial design for General Electric Company and its Hotpoint division. "But for those who don't or can't use the new leisure, there will be the 11 a.m. cocktail, bridge every day and the casual affair on the side."

Some people also wonder about the extent to which

the poor will share in the household technological revolution. It's estimated that at present one in four United States families lives in slum tenements, farm shanties or other dilapidated housing. Economists predict that all Americans will live better in the years ahead as the country as a whole produces more and grows more affluent. But it's likely many of the advances that will make the home a pleasanter place for the vast middle class will remain beyond the reach of lower-income families.

Says University of Pittsburgh anthropologist Arthur Tuden: "There is a sharp cleavage between income groups now, and my feeling is that there won't be much change in coming decades."

This is not to say the poor won't get better housing. An immense amount of housing will be built in the United States between now and the end of the century, and in the course of this construction effort roughly a quarter of existing houses and apartments—including almost all those now considered substandard—will be replaced.

This replacement task, coupled with the need for additional housing to accommodate the population increase, will require the construction of at least 60 million new dwellings in the United States by 2000. As William R. Ewald, a Washington, D.C., planner, puts it, "For every residence that exists today, we're going to have to build at least one other" by 2000.

Finding land for all this new housing will pose a problem. Sites are already scarce in the urban areas where most of the new residences will be needed. The result will be more multi-family construction.

Currently about three in every four Americans live in detached single-family homes. "By 2000," says Alfred Eckersburg, vice president of Real Estate Research Corporation of Chicago, a leading housing research firm, "single-family dwellings will be only half of all housing." The other half will be apartments, attached townhouses, duplexes and the like.

The trend to multi-family dwellings may be accelerated "if there is a political decision that we cannot afford urban sprawl because land has become too precious," adds Mr. Eckersburg. He notes that even now strict laws limiting single-family housing are common throughout Europe.

The swing to multi-family construction is already pronounced in the United States. In 1955 only 10% of new housing units built were apartments and duplexes. In 1966 the proportion was 35%, according to the National Association of Home Builders.

The multi-family trend obviously will change the look of the landscape to some extent. But there is no unanimity on how much housing will change in appearance or on how much construction methods of the future will differ from those used today.

Designer Paul McCobb expects great change. He en-

visions large numbers of factory-made houses of striking contemporary design. Prefabricated wall panels and
other components would eliminate most on-site labor.
"Building houses by hand as we do is ludicrous," he
argues.

If Mr. McCobb's predictions come true, many home
buyers around the turn of the century will purchase
"modular units," or rooms, from a factory. Each room
will come completely wired and equipped with necessary plumbing and appliances. A newly married couple
might start with a utility core room, living room,
kitchen, bedroom and bathroom and then add other
rooms later. In Philco's dream house, which consists of
modular units, all the rooms are six-sided. This allows
them to be fitted together in an endless variety of floor
plans, with each room having access to as many as six
others.

But many authorities in the housing field doubt that
modular construction or other bold innovations in
building will have a significant impact any time soon.
Buyer resistance to radical departures from tradition in
architecture partly explains this view. Another factor
is the hesitancy of builders to adopt new methods.

Albert Dietz, a professor of architecture and civil
engineering at Massachusetts Institute of Technology
and an expert on the use of plastics in building, foresees a gradual movement in architecture to "more rational design," but he believes the exteriors of houses

will change only in a slow, evolutionary way. "Builders simply have found it cheaper to build conventionally," he says. "We're not going to have a revolution in architecture in the next 30 years."

David Plumb, a plastics division executive at Monsanto Company, a chemical producer, agrees with Mr. Dietz. "I'd guess that 30 years from now there'll still be an awful lot of Cape Cods built," he comments.

His view is surprising, for Monsanto at one time ballyhooed a largely plastic "house of the future" as an alternative to board-by-board and brick-by-brick construction. More than a decade ago Monsanto erected a plastic house at Disneyland in California. With four white wings of fiber glass-reinforced plastic cantilevered out from a concrete core, the house looks something like a giant white mushroom. Visitors seem to like it, and it has worn well.

But Mr. Plumb says the dwelling was "prohibitively expensive" to build, and he indicates Monsanto is not optimistic about bringing the cost down to a level where it would be competitive with that of a conventional house. Even with volume production, the plastic house would cost "a minimum of $25 a square foot," compared with as little as $8 for a frame house, says Mr. Plumb.

Although predictions of startling transformations in housing designs provoke widespread skepticism, there is general agreement that prefabrication will loom steadily larger. Most authorities doubt this trend will take the direction forecast by Mr. McCobb and Philco; the dissenters from the McCobb-Philco view of the future say that when Americans need more room or rise in the world, they are more likely to move to a new house and a new neighborhood—as they usually do at present—than to add new modular sections. But these housing experts do say that factory-built homes similar to those produced today and prefabricated housing components will become more commonplace.

Prefabrication already has made big gains. The Home Manufacturers Association, a trade group, estimates that 24% of housing starts in 1965 were prefabricated, double the proportion six years earlier. These figures actually understate the role of prefabrication in housing, since they ignore the growing use of factory-made components such as pre-hung doors and windows in conventional construction.

New materials are also certain to win wider acceptance in housing. Plastics and aluminum will come into far greater use for siding and interior panels that will never need painting. In some homes the owners will be able to move the new interior panels about to rearrange space. Glass will be used more extensively, particularly if glass-makers can lower the costs of newly developed windows that can be adjusted to allow varying amounts of light to enter a room or to change the color of the light.

A lot of these materials will go into second homes (which are not included in the projection of a minimum of 60 million new dwellings by 2000). Barclay G. Jones, associate director of the Center for Housing and Environmental Studies at Cornell University, goes so far as to predict that by 2000 "the average American family will own two housing units, often in two distant locations." He notes that in this country there already is a housing unit for every 3.4 people and says the ratio may approach one unit for every two persons by the end of the century.

Underlying this forecast is the belief that a couple of decades from now, with suburbs extending much farther out than they do now, more people will be attracted by the convenience of life in apartments and duplexes in rebuilt city centers. Then, with their increased affluence and lengthened holidays, they will seek privately owned retreats in mountains and forests and at the shore.

"I think it will result in a more satisfying life of greater extremes," observes Mr. Jones. "A two-house family will split their life between intensely urban experiences and real rural life, rather than today's miserable compromise of city and country in some suburb."

Wherever families live in the year 2000, the mechanics of life will consume far less of their time than they do now. Consider the matter of keeping a house and the things in it clean.

145

Besides the electrostatic air filters and the sonic cleaners, which Philco says will be installed at entrances to remove dust from clothes with ultrasonic waves, there may be vibrating floor grills by doors to clean shoes. For the kitchen Philco has designed the dish-molding machine; the company says disposable plates, bowls and cups for everyday use could be made for a few pennies a meal. Short of this, appliance manu-facturers are toying with the idea of dishwashers that would supplement water and detergent action with ultrasonic waves capable of removing the most stub-born egg stains. Mr. Sandin of GE predicts that within the next few decades beams of searing light will vapor-ize all refuse in many households.

Cooking will be revolutionized, too. The microwave oven, long available but, at $1,000 and up, too ex-pensive for home use, will finally begin to appear in the family kitchen. Raytheon Company, which de-veloped commercial microwave ovens, says it probably will market a home model for less than $500 within a year. Raytheon foresees further substantial reductions and a mass market within five to ten years.

Microwave ovens cook food from the inside out by agitating it with microwave energy. They are extremely fast. A microwave oven can thoroughly cook a three-pound pork roast in 30 minutes, compared with three hours in a conventional oven. Bacon takes only 30 sec-onds.

One trouble is that microwaves don't change meat color; a cooked roast or steak looks raw. A gas or electric browning unit can be added to darken the outside, but the red interior still bothers some people. One solution may be kitchens with two ovens—a microwave one for fish, casseroles and reheating leftovers or thawing frozen cooked foods and a conventional one for steaks, roasts and fowl.

Philco designers, along with their counterparts at GE, have moved a step beyond the microwave oven in their planning by combining it with a freezer. By pushing a few buttons, the housewife could select portions of frozen foods and transfer them to slots in the microwave oven, where automatic controls would heat them to precisely the right temperature.

Besides doing more jobs and doing them better, household appliances of the future will be more reliable than today's models—or so manufacturers claim. This improvement will result from advances in solid-state electronics. These include transistorized controls to replace electro-mechanical switches and the still more foolproof "integrated circuits," tiny devices that eventually will supplant the transistorized controls in consumer products. Solid-state devices can repeat an operation—such as opening and closing an electric circuit—millions of times with no sign of wear.

Transistorized controls have been used in radios, phonographs and television sets for some time. Last

147

year they became available on clothes washers. Unlike electro-mechanical switches, which have a limited number of positions, the new washer controls allow "tuning" for any size of load or gentleness of agitation. Such precision is useful for small loads. "You can put four inches of water in the machine and wash two pairs of socks," says an official of one appliance manufacturer.

Transistorized controls now add about $50 to the retail prices of the washers, but costs of solid-state devices are expected to come down fast. Cheap integrated circuits, besides contributing to the reliability and versatility of appliances, will help drive down the costs of computers to the point where homes can be linked to bank computers that will handle financial transactions electronically, school computers and "time-sharing" computer centers.

The spectacular innovations forecast in the home entertainment field could focus more leisure and social activities in the home. As electronic devices pipe more and better entertainment and education into the home, some experts foresee less demand for outside activities such as movies, concerts and live theater.

The video tape recorder could have great impact in the home within the next decade. Sony Corporation, a Japanese firm, marketed the first home recorder, a black-and-white model, in 1965.

Prices are still high. Sony's lowest-priced 1966 model cost $1,240, and a color recorder may sell for twice that.

But major companies in the electronics field are working hard to drive costs down to levels where they will attract a mass market. F. R. Amthor, a Westinghouse Electric Corporation consumer products executive, looks for color recorders selling for less than $1,000 before long. "When you see people laying out $600 to $800 for color TV, video tape is within reach," he says. Illinois Institute of Technology researchers already claim to have developed a color video recorder that could be produced for under $500.

Video recorders work much like ordinary tape recorders, except that both sound and pictures are put on magnetic tape. The recorder can preserve television shows for later playback or home "movies" taken with a TV camera. The tapes can be viewed on a television set.

People who are enthusiastic about video recorders say the devices could result in improved television programs. Networks could beam shows that appeal to limited audiences—opera or serious drama, for example —at odd hours, such as 4 a.m. Recorders equipped with timers would tape the show, and the viewer could later watch it at his convenience.

Equally attractive is the prospect that pre-recorded tapes will be sold by stores or rented by libraries. This could make available in the home complex educational courses that require visual demonstrations, as well as hit Broadway shows and other entertainment.

149

In hopes of cutting the cost of buying or borrowing pre-recorded television programs, researchers now are trying to develop pressed discs similar to phonograph records that would do the same job as video tapes. Records could be produced from a master disc for a fraction of the cost of making tapes, according to the researchers.

Some marketing men see the day when homes will have video tape equipment for home recordings and video record players for pre-recorded material. Video records are far from perfected, but Westinghouse has succeeded in combining still pictures with sound on a record, while Sony has put moving pictures on records in experiments.

Electronics engineers are confident television sets will improve dramatically. Within the next decade or so, TV receivers will change from bulky pieces of furniture to shallow screens that will be mounted on walls, they say. This will be accomplished by substituting a handful of integrated circuits for today's picture tube. The wall sets will produce pictures of greater clarity and purer color than is now attainable, say researchers. Screens measuring two-feet-by-three-feet are likely sometime in the 1970s, and the larger ones will become available later.

The final television breakthrough in this century most likely will be the application of holography—a new science that uses beams of laser light to create three-dimensional images—in TV broadcasting and receiving. Says Robert C. Wilson, general manager of GE's consumer electronics division: "We know that by the beginning of the Twenty-first Century we will be able to buy a television set that will fill one wall of the living room with a three-dimensional color picture."

—HERBERT G. LAWSON

Education:

The Lifelong School

"We are now founding colleges at the rate of 20 or more a year," says Frank Bowles, one of the Ford Foundation's top education specialists. "I believe that within 10 years we will be founding them at the rate of one a week."

And that only begins to suggest the magnitude of the growth and change American education will undergo in the next few decades.

Enrollments at all levels will soar. Census Bureau forecasts indicate the United States school-age population (5 to 24) will swell to more than 125 million by the year 2000 from 70.2 million in early 1967. The proportion of this group actually in the classroom will climb because of the surge in college undergraduate and graduate study. Moreover, the young people will be joined in the pursuit of education by rising numbers of adults.

The nature of instruction will change, too. The stress will be on flexibility. Students will move from lectures and demonstrations by master teachers in giant lecture halls to intimate seminar rooms to cubicles equipped with every sort of electronic teaching aid. Rigid class levels will disappear and students will advance at their own speed: a 12-year-old might be an eighth grader in mathematics, a seventh grader in history and a sixth grader in English.

Computers will be the key to this individualized education. Teaching machines plugged into computers will drill youngsters in arithmetic, grammar and reading skills, grading them and correcting their mistakes instantly. Robert D. Tschirgi, dean of academic planning and professor of physiology and anatomy at the University of California's Berkeley campus, calls the computer "the greatest thing to hit education since Johann Gutenberg invented movable type."

Educational content as well as methods will change in fundamental fashion between now and the end of the century. Education authorities say this change will be forced by rapid technological developments that will outmode specific skills learned in the classroom. Curriculums will emphasize teaching not what the facts are but how students can gather the facts they need, analyze them and make decisions. Instead of swallowing a predigested textbook version of George Washington's role in American history, for example, students might be told to dig into several sources and come up with their own appraisal of his career.

"We simply can't continue to provide the facts

needed to make decisions in a world where most of the facts we'll need are still unknown," says Nolan Estes, an official of the United States Office of Education.

By learning how to learn, people will fit themselves for the constant reeducation necessary if they are to continue to play useful roles in the economy, educators say. "We are in the early stages of a technological world that is going to require essentially all people to have to go to school continually to stay abreast of the changes," says Harold Clark, professor of educational economics at Columbia University's Teachers College.

This educational updating process, which will be carried on at work and in the home, often by electronic means, as well as in formal classrooms, is part of the explanation for the anticipated increase in adult education. But another factor in this increase will be expanded leisure, which is expected to lead to more demand for adult education unrelated to practical ends. Such a prospect causes one educator to wax eloquent. "In the world of 2000," he says, "we may look for a return to the ancient values of the pursuit of truth and beauty—of enlightenment for its own sake."

The increased demand for education of all types means that education will assume new importance in the economy. Salaries, construction and other expenditures for formal education now account for more than 6% of the $739.5 billion gross national product. Some Office of Education officials estimate that such outlays will generate as much as 25% of the $2.3 trillion GNP expected in 2000. How much expenditures for instruction outside regular classrooms will rise is anybody's guess, but the increase is sure to be immense.

"It is apparent that education will be the new dynamic of our national economy—that learning is the new growth industry," says Harold B. Gores, president of Educational Facilities Laboratories Incorporated, a nonprofit corporation established by the Ford Foundation.

That the Federal Government and industry will bulk larger in education in the future is accepted as certain even by educators who are uneasy about the trend, which promises to weaken their control over schooling. Federal officials insist the Government will remain a "junior partner" in education, concerned mainly with financing, and corporate executives say industry's function will continue to be to supply whatever educational materials teachers want. But it is clear both Government and industry will play increasingly active parts in deciding what schools will teach and how they will present it.

Litton Industries Incorporated, Burroughs Corporation and several other firms already are deeply involved in education through their operation of antipoverty Job Corps centers. A number of electronics companies and business machine makers have plunged into educational markets through mergers and acquisitions. The

155

Government intends to use new educational research and development centers it is opening across the country to speed the introduction of new teaching techniques and equipment in schools.

This Federal effort to accelerate educational innovation, which is paralleled by prodding administered by private foundations in the form of pilot projects and demonstration grants, must contend with education's traditional resistance to change. "The aircraft industry would go out of business in two years if it changed as slowly as education," says Loyd Turner, president of the Fort Worth, Texas, school board and assistant to the president of General Dynamics Corporation.

But the innovators aim to break this pattern. One of their top-priority goals is to capitalize on the computer's capabilities in education.

The machines won't replace teachers. John Walton, chairman of Johns Hopkins University's education department, says they will be used "the same way totalizators are used at the race track to figure odds, payoffs and so forth. The heroes there are still the jockeys and horses, just as teachers and students will continue to be the heroes in the classroom while the gadgetry handles a lot of the drudgery."

The gadgetry still must be perfected, but no one doubts this will be done within the next few years. Manufacturers already have devised computer-run teaching machines that respond to spoken, written, typed or push-button questions and answer by flashing slides and movies on a screen, sending teletypewriter messages and even by talking back with prerecorded vocabularies.

"You can have a friendly relationship with a computer that a teacher couldn't find time for," says G. E. Callahan, educational marketing specialist with American Telephone and Telegraph Company. "It's never impatient, and the computer remembers exactly what each kid it is tutoring knows."

Computerized education will take place in the home as well as in the classroom. Youngsters will drill in basic subjects at home, guided by school computers linked to a teletypewriter or other types of outlets in the home. Library data retrieval services and commercial home-learning courses will be available over the same sort of network. Tomorrow's encyclopedia might be sold as a subscription service that would give customers instant access to any piece of information stored by the encyclopedia publisher's computer.

Technological innovations in education won't be limited to computers. Overhead projectors that show close-ups of materials on the teacher's desk and enlarge microscopic views of laboratory experiments will supplement blackboards. Closed-circuit television and picture-phone communications will make lectures and demonstrations by outstanding teachers available to many students in classrooms across the nation simultaneously. Video-tape presentations of everything from erupting volcanoes to historical skits will enliven instruction.

Advancing technology will greatly influence the design of tomorrow's schools. Logan Wilson, president of the American Council on Education, a professional organization, cautions that "before we begin to visualize strange egg-shaped structures in which students of 1984 may painlessly acquire knowledge, we might remind ourselves that a good deal of teaching still goes on in buildings erected before 1894."

But new schools, to a considerable extent, will have to be built around the electronic gear that will cram them. Moreover, the future schools will reflect the stress on flexibility in instruction, with sliding partitions and easily removable equipment permitting the use of space for many purposes. At the flip of a switch, for example, an auditorium might convert into a dozen small lecture halls.

Many planners predict that more and more communities will concentrate all levels of school facilities in centrally located "educational parks." This concept goes against the tradition of small neighborhood schools for elementary pupils and requires more transportation for youngsters. But advocates say educational parks will eliminate needless duplication of costly facilities and allow top teachers to reach larger numbers of pupils. They also see such consolidation as a way to end de facto school segregation and eliminate poor quality schools in slums and rural areas.

East Orange, New Jersey, plans to have its dozen city schools combined into a single "educational plaza" by 1980. Multi-storied schools will cover much of the 18-acre campus, with playgrounds located on the roofs of some buildings. Big city educational parks might stack their schools in skyscrapers, planners suggest, while small communities might strive for settings resembling today's college campuses.

Most authorities think that within the next couple of decades compulsory public schooling will begin at age four and continue through the equivalent of two years of college. The introduction of compulsory post-high school training means a vast expansion of junior colleges, often called community colleges. Some educators believe every town of 50,000 population will need at least one community college.

These institutions will prepare many students to take jobs at the end of two years. The schools will become a prime source of medical technicians, data-processing specialists, electronics repairmen and other specialists critically needed in a scientific, automated age. Community colleges also will provide the first two years of college for perhaps half of all those youngsters working for bachelor's degrees; these students will transfer to universities for the remaining two years.

Edmund J. Gleazer Jr., director of the American

Association of Junior Colleges, sees tomorrow's community colleges as "educational service stations," open year-round, seven days a week and late into the night. They would be places where adults could go to retrain and upgrade themselves for changing job needs and to learn just for personal satisfaction.

Faculties will include businessmen and technicians who teach part-time for "the personal sense of reward, plus a fair salary, and as a way to keep current in their own specialized fields," says Mr. Gleazer. Curriculums will "get away from the idea of 50-minute classes, one-year courses and offer lots of short-term programs," he adds.

Mr. Gleazer expects all higher education gradually to "get away from the formalities we now have for entering and the great ritual of getting out." This will be necessary in a society where job requirements are changed rapidly by technological advances and where even college-trained specialists may find their skills made obsolete several times during their working years, many educators say. Mr. Gleazer argues that higher education must be opened up so someone can study, go out and work and still get back "into the stream again" without being blocked by credit requirements, prerequisites and other formalities.

Many universities are likely to drop their two lower years as a result of community college expansion. On the other hand, at many universities two years or more of graduate study in specialized fields may well become almost routine. Postgraduate universities to explore the frontiers of knowledge will spring up, too; Rockefeller University (formerly Rockefeller Institute), whose research facilities in New York City have been the scene of notable advances in medical research and natural sciences, is considered a forerunner of this type of postgraduate institution.

Some smaller private universities seem doomed by current trends. For many of them tuition from freshman and sophomore courses, which are highly standardized and taught to large groups, is the difference between balanced budgets and operating losses. In addition, says Milton S. Eisenhower, retired president of Johns Hopkins, "it is questionable whether private philanthropy will continue to support as many private institutions as it has up to now."

Essentially, say educators, the situation among United States universities is that the rich are getting richer—and the poor are getting relatively poorer. Prestigious private schools and big state universities are attracting disproportionately large shares of philanthropic and government funds, it's said, with the result that any smaller institutions lag ever further behind in caliber of staff and facilities.

Some educators are highly critical of this trend. They say it concentrates too much power and influence in a few universities and tends to create a sort of "class system" that stigmatizes many lesser-known schools and their graduates. They also say the uneven distribution of private and Federal largess is leading to the atrophying of many small institutions that could fulfill a useful function if given adequate help.

Earl J. McGrath, director of the Institute of Higher Education at Columbia University Teachers College, is particularly disturbed by the "elitist philosophy" that he says guides the distribution of massive Federal support to a clique of big-name universities. "The hundreds of millions of Federal dollars for research flow primarily to a few universities and to a few departments within them, and often only to a select group within these departments," says Mr. McGrath.

He estimates 10 top schools (among them: Massachusetts Institute of Technology, Harvard and the University of California) soak up nearly 40% of the funds. One hundred universities—out of a total of 1,100 four-year institutions in the United States—receive all but 10% of the money.

This concentration of resources is expected to lead to more "multiversities"—the name coined by former University of California President Clark Kerr for immense institutions like the 87,000-student, nine-campus school he headed. At such huge institutions, there is always the danger that the students will feel they are reduced to mere ciphers; this mood is generally given at least part of the blame for the riots that rocked the Berkeley campus of the University of California.

But some educators say the impact of bigness can be eased by dividing the large schools into a number of relatively small, self-contained undergraduate colleges. This is the approach already being taken at such universities as Michigan State, Florida State and Rutgers, and other institutions are likely to follow suit.

Educators also say the electronic gear that will make possible individualized instruction in lower grades will serve the same function in universities, further lessening the impact of mammoth enrollments. In dormitory rooms equipped with picture phones, teletypewriters and perhaps facsimile reproducers, students will be able to watch video-taped lectures, summon up research data and follow computerized instruction in languages, sciences and other courses.

College enrollments are due to rise far faster than the school population generally. Undergraduate ranks are expected to reach 15 million to 20 million by 2000, up from 5.5 million in 1967. Graduate students are expected to number between 2 million and 2.5 million by the close of the century, compared with 520,000 in 1967.

The new classrooms and dormitories such enrollment growth will demand stagger the imagination. Economist Peter F. Drucker has calculated that to make

163

room for the more than 9 million students who will be crowding into colleges and universities as early as 1975, the United States must add facilities equal to twice all the campus buildings erected since Harvard University opened its doors in 1636.

None of this takes into account the vast expansion of corporate programs for advanced education of their own employes. Xerox Corporation already runs "what amounts to an internal university," with nearly 4,500 employes enrolled this year, says Joseph C. Wilson, chairman. Many other companies have similarly extensive educational programs.

Says Frank Bowles of the Ford Foundation: "I think there's a very good possibility that company operations will get to be so educationally competent that they will become degree-granting."

—RICHARD MARTIN

Medicine:

More Healthy Years

"The runny nose will still be running in 2000," predicts a medical researcher.

But he and other scientists agree that in more important areas the next few decades will see immense strides in medicine. Heart disease will all but disappear as a serious health menace in the United States, they believe. The cure rate for cancer will climb. Arthritis will be wiped out. New vaccines will eliminate hepatitis and other viral diseases.

Medical advances also will result in greater control over the beginnings of life. Feeble-mindedness and other inherited abnormalities may be prevented by drugs administered while the baby is still in the mother's womb. Parents may be able to pick the sex of their offspring. Artificial "wombs" will save some premature infants that now have no chance of survival.

None of which is to say that the common cold will be the only medical problem left unsolved by the end of this century. Most researchers, for example, doubt medicine will conquer the aging process to a degree suffi-

165

cient to push the average life span far beyond the proverbial three score and 10 years, despite the periodic predictions of a few scientists that men as a matter of course someday will live 100 or even 150 years.

A large portion of the impoverished masses living in the world's underdeveloped lands will continue to benefit little or not at all from medical advances. Even in the United States and other wealthy nations there will still be illness—most notably, some cases of cancer —that resist treatment.

Nevertheless, optimism predominates in most medical authorities' forecasts. "We've got research tools and techniques, such as extremely precise laboratory measurements, that we never had before," says one scientist. Dr. James Shannon, director of the National Institutes of Health, feels that the Federal Government's massive investment in training researchers in recent years is bound to pay off dramatically. "We've built up a tremendous research base," he says.

One universally predicted advance is a sharp decline in "premature" deaths—such as a fatal heart attack at age 50. Heart disease is now the No. 1 killer in the United States, causing 55% of all deaths.

Mechanical devices to assist failing hearts offer one approach to cutting this toll. The replacement of worn-out heart valves with artificial plastic substitutes already is relatively common. Now heart specialists are making progress in efforts to develop external pumps that could take over the work of ailing hearts temporarily.

Dr. Michael DeBakey, the noted Houston heart surgeon, used such a heart-assist device in treating a woman who had just undergone an operation to replace two heart valves severely damaged by rheumatic fever. The purpose was to rest her heart and thereby aid her recovery (she did, in fact, recover).

The pump procedure is still highly experimental and some physicians are skeptical about its effectiveness at this stage. But heart experts feel the pumps eventually will prove their value. The National Heart Institute, part of the NIH, is stepping up research on assist devices, and Dr. Donald Fredrickson, director, predicts that "we'll probably have the devices ready for broad use sometime in the next several years."

Permanent replacement of the entire diseased heart is a more distant possibility. Transplantation of hearts from deceased persons is not ruled out, assuming, as most researchers do, that a way will be found to overcome the body's resistance to "foreign" tissue. But organ transplantation is likely to be less important in the heart field than in the treatment of much rarer cases where such organs as the liver, kidney or pancreas are damaged beyond repair by disease or other causes. Although it might be feasible to store enough of these organs in organ "banks" to meet the relatively limited need, the supply of healthy hearts for transplantation

167

would be extremely short in relation to the number of heart-disease victims.

An artificial heart would overcome this problem and some researchers are confident such a device will be a reality by 1980.

Dr. Frank Hastings, chief of the National Heart Institute's artificial heart program, says the artificial heart essentially would be a plastic or rubber pump implanted in the body. At first the pump probably would be powered by batteries that an individual might carry in a pocket; power would be transmitted through the skin by radio waves.

Ultimately, says Dr. Hastings, tiny power sources would be implanted in the body. The artificial heart would be controlled by electronic instruments, also in the body, that would measure blood pressure and automatically adjust the pump's output accordingly.

Impressive as such an achievement would be, the very idea of taking out the human heart and replacing it causes many laymen—and some doctors—to recoil. Fortunately for all concerned, artificial hearts, along with transplants and assist devices, are likely to be largely obsolete by the end of the century.

By then, researchers agree, heart disease will be preventable or curable by other means. As NIH Director Shannon puts it, "we won't need a spare parts department in our hospitals" for most cardiac patients.

Drugs that reduce blood pressure already are sharply

cutting deaths from some forms of the diseases of the heart and the circulatory system. "Although it has virtually escaped public notice, deaths from both high blood pressure and strokes have dropped dramatically," says Dr. John Sampson of the University of California's medical school.

Between 1950 and 1964, the annual stroke death rate in the United States for males aged 45 through 64 dropped from 128 per 100,000 to 94, while the high blood pressure death rate for males in the same age bracket fell from 95 per 100,000 to 43. Death rates for women dropped even more sharply.

Researchers are confident they can make even more impressive progress against the most common type of heart disease—a buildup of fatty deposits that clogs blood vessels, restricts the flow of blood to the heart muscle and causes heart attacks. The effort to get rid of these deposits primarily involves educating people to avoid some types of food and developing drugs to reduce the level of certain fats in the blood. Among these fats is cholesterol, which has been associated with fatty deposit accumulations.

Heart-disease drugs now in use or emerging from the laboratory undoubtedly will be succeeded by even more effective ones. And researchers hope progress in drugs will be paralleled by changes in "environmental factors," such as cigaret smoking and lack of exercise, that are believed to contribute to heart trouble. The

169

upshot, according to Dr. Irvine Page of the Cleveland Clinic, is that "between changed environmental factors and better drugs, coronary heart disease will be pretty well licked by 2000."

Cancer researchers generally shy from such sweeping statements. They fear some forms of cancer, such as a bone cancer known as osteogenic sarcoma, may remain incurable in 2000 if not caught until they have spread widely through the body.

All the same, cancer will be overcome to a substantial extent by a variety of weapons, including improved prevention, detection, surgery, radiation, drug therapy and stimulation of natural body defenses. The cure rate, currently about a third of the cases, is expected to double by the close of the century. And this forecast does not take into account the many cases that will be prevented entirely.

Prevention will greatly reduce the incidence of lung cancer, the principal cancer killer of males, researchers forecast. Top scientists at Sloan-Kettering Institute in New York City and Roswell Park Memorial Institute in Buffalo, both major cancer study centers, assert that additional medical studies will—in their view—continue to incriminate cigarets as a cause of lung cancer. Education programs will "finally convince the majority of smokers to either stop smoking or change to pipes or safer cigarets," asserts Dr. Joseph Burchenal, a vice president at Sloan-Kettering.

Diagnosis at an early stage, when treatment can be

more effective, will help fight other cancers, such as cancer of the cervix and breast in women. Early detection depends in part on encouraging people to take advantage of diagnostic techniques available today, but improved X-rays and other new diagnostic tools also will help catch the disease more quickly. A new type of blood test now under development may prove useful for some forms of cancer that are particularly hard to detect, such as cancer of the pancreas.

Spotting cancer cells before they spread to a large area will increase the rate of cures by surgery and radiation therapy. Radiation treatment will be further improved by new machines capable of delivering doses of radiation that are stronger and more precisely aimed at cancerous tissues than those produced by present equipment.

Thus far the search for drugs effective against cancer has been nearly fruitless. With the exception of agents that cure skin cancer, choriocarcinoma (a rare cancer that attacks the placenta) and a very few cases of leukemia and lymph cancer, drugs only alleviate symptoms and delay somewhat the fatal outcome.

Nevertheless, scientists believe anti-cancer drugs far superior to most available now will be developed by 2000. One substance attracting interest is called L-asparaginase; used in mice, it appears to be highly effective against leukemia, which affects the blood-forming system.

What particularly excites researchers is that L-aspar-

171

aginase is "the first agent known to be active against malignant cells alone," says Dr. Edward Boyse of Sloan-Kettering. Other leukemia drugs seem to attack all cells, though they affect leukemic cells more than others; this broad, unselective toxicity severely limits their use. Researchers caution that the promise L-asparaginase appears to hold may well evaporate once it is tried in man, but this does not diminish their conviction that powerful cancer drugs eventually will be found.

The new drugs will be bolstered by new techniques to stimulate the body's own natural resistance to disease. Dr. George Moore, director of the Roswell Park institute, says these might involve removing cancer cells from a patient and increasing their "strangeness" to his body by radiation or chemical treatment. The cells would then be replaced in the patient, where they would trigger the body's mechanism for rejecting foreign tissue. The body would thus be induced to intensify its fight against the cancer.

Doctors divide over the chances for developing a vaccine against cancer. Ever since clues popped up that leukemia might be caused by a virus, there has been speculation over the likelihood of such a vaccine.

Some experts are pessimistic. They note that isolation of a virus that causes cancer in man—a prerequisite for a vaccine—still eludes researchers. They also suggest that not one but several viruses may be involved, compounding the difficulty of vaccine research.

But other scientists remain optimistic. Dr. Moore,

172

for one, thinks that by 2000 some cancers will definitely be linked to viruses or virus-like agents and that effective vaccines will be developed.

Turning from cancer to less dread diseases, researchers say they are convinced colds are caused by viruses. But the almost unanimous judgment is that there is scant hope of coming up with a vaccine that would prevent colds. The reason is that the guilty viruses are so numerous—perhaps running into the hundreds—that it would be impossible to produce a vaccine offering protection against all of them.

On the other hand, researchers are almost certain to come up with vaccines for some other viral illnesses. Merck and Company scientists are well along in development of a vaccine against mumps, which, though usually a minor disease in children, often has serious complications in adults. Doctors at the NIH have had promising results with a vaccine for German measles; when pregnant women are afflicted with this disease, their offspring frequently have serious defects.

Two Australian researchers have suggested that viral diseases other than measles may also be implicated in birth defects. In particular, they think there may be a relationship between infectious hepatitis, a viral infection of the liver for which a vaccine may be ready before 1980, and mongolism, which causes 6,000 infants a year in the United States alone to be born as deformed, incurable idiots.

The Australians say the same sort of relationship

173

that appears to exist between hepatitis in the mother and mongolism in the child may extend to other viral illnesses and other abnormalities. Thus, new vaccines against viral ills may yield unexpected dividends by eliminating many congenital defects.

Birth defects also may decline as a result of the use of drugs to affect the action of the genetic materials that guide the development of the fetus. Researchers have a long way to go before such techniques are feasible, but they believe they are making headway.

"The activities of harmful dominant genes could in theory be repressed as desired, or inactive genes could be turned back on or derepressed as needed," says Dr. Edward Tatum, a Nobel prize winner in genetics and a researcher at Rockefeller University in New York. Medical tests would disclose whether an unborn child had genetic defects necessitating treatment.

Selecting the sex of a child is another feat that many scientists are convinced will be possible someday. It would be done by separating the sperm carrying male chromosomes from sperm carrying female chromosomes and using artificial insemination. Just when this will be practicable is uncertain. "It might be in next week's medical journal," says Robert Davies, a biochemist at the University of Pennsylvania. But other researchers think control over an offspring's sex is far off, although they agree it will come before 2000.

Another research effort involving the beginning of

174

life is under way at Stanford University's medical school in Palo Alto, California. Scientists there have devised an artificial womb that they hope will be the forerunner of equipment to save infants born too prematurely to live in present incubators and with present techniques.

Stanford's artificial womb is a steel tank with a glass porthole; it looks like an oversized diver's helmet. The tank contains a solution under pressure so high it drives through the fetus's skin the oxygen that normally would be received via the umbilical cord. Doctors at Stanford have tried the chamber for about 50 fetuses over the past four years. Some of the fetuses' hearts have continued to beat as long as four days, but no fetus has survived.

Still, scientists believe the artificial womb can be perfected. "Within about a decade we'll be able to save some babies born as early as the 20th week of pregnancy," one Stanford physician predicts. Now fetuses usually don't survive if born before the 31st week, so such an artificial womb would save thousands of babies now doomed. Some 800,000 to 1,000,000 babies are known to be miscarried every year in the United States.

Medical scientists studying the aging process are much less hopeful of achieving startling changes than are researchers focusing on the beginning of life. It's true that life expectancy (now 67 years for men and 74 for women in the United States) will rise as heart

175

disease, cancer and other ills kill fewer people and the general level of health improves. The increase probably won't be spectacular, however.

"We may have an additional 10 years, but I don't expect anything like a 50% increase," says Dr. Nathan Shock of Baltimore, a top researcher on aging.

Aging is still largely a mystery. "We don't have the faintest idea what causes aging," says Dr. Shock. One theory holds that genes trigger aging just as they control the development of new life. An opposing theory suggests that a wearing out of genetic material, with the subsequent introduction of genetic errors, is responsible for physical deterioration in old age.

Unsure of the cause of the aging process, scientists are handicapped in seeking ways to prevent or even delay it. Thus, it's likely that a generation from now men will continue to grow frail in their 70s and 80s, susceptible to severe effects from even mild diseases and to fatal failure of vital organs.

But while men may not live to 100 as a matter of course in the foreseeable future, their final years may well become more meaningful and pleasant as a result of scientific advances. Dr. Shock says that the new drugs to cut fatty deposits in the blood will reduce senility as well as heart disease. They will accomplish this by insuring a free flow of blood to the brain, whose function is now often impaired by fatty deposits that diminish its blood supply. Research also is under way on other types of drugs designed to keep the minds of older persons sharp.

The elderly also will be the chief beneficiaries of the anticipated conquest of arthritis. Some nine million Americans now suffer from the crippling effects of the disease. Researchers say osteo-arthritis, a form of the ailment in which the cartilage simply wears out with old age, eventually will be prevented by chemical treatments. Rheumatoid arthritis, an inflammatory type of the disease that afflicts all ages but reaches its most advanced stage in older people, is expected to yield to a vaccine or to new antibiotic drugs.

"These developments will mean that we just won't have arthritis in 2000," declares Dr. William Clark, president of the Arthritis Foundation.

The optimism that pervades most discussions of the future of medicine in the United States fades when the talk turns to the outlook for less advanced sections of the globe.

True, there will be some progress. "Certain of the killing diseases will be cut down by medical tools we already have," says Dr. Thomas Weller, an expert on tropical medicine at Harvard. Vaccines now available, Dr. Weller explains, will continue to reduce smallpox overseas and soon will just about eliminate common measles, which currently kills many children in Africa.

But any drastic improvement in the health of poorer nations would require changing the sanitary practices

177

of whole populations—a task that "could take centuries," in the view of Dr. G. Robert Coatney, a tropical health researcher at Louisiana State University.

Another essential for substantially better health in underdeveloped areas is alleviation of the chronic malnutrition that leaves millions easy prey to disease. This diet improvement may or may not come by 2000, depending on factors ranging from politics to birth rates.

Diseases long since conquered in the United States still ravage backward areas. There are now 15 million to 20 million cases of tuberculosis in the world; as many as 3 million people will die from TB in the next 12 months. Diarrhea each year kills 5 million people, mostly children. Prospects for a quick reduction in the death rate from these diseases, both easily preventable or curable, are dim.

Many underdeveloped lands probably will also continue to be plagued with diseases peculiar to them. Trachoma, an infection of the eye, currently afflicts some 500 million people in Africa, Asia and parts of South America. Six million of these victims are substantially blinded by the disease, and millions more have impaired vision. About 150 million people in Africa, the Mideast and parts of South America and Southeast Asia are infected with schistosomiasis, a parasitic disease that causes extreme lethargy.

Health officials are making headway against malaria. There were 100 million cases and 900,000 deaths in

1965, compared with 300 million cases and 3 million deaths 20 years earlier, according to the World Health Organization. Some nations where malaria has been a serious problem, such as India, are well on the way to controlling the disease. But researchers aren't hopeful that the WHO's goal of eradicating malaria from most areas of the world by 1980 will be met.

—WILLIAM M. CARLEY

War:

Tomorrow's Arms

In late 1963 Pentagon reporters gathered in the office of the Secretary of the Navy for what was billed as a social visit with the newly named commandant of the Marine Corps, Gen. Wallace M. Greene Jr. But the gathering turned into a working session for the reporters as Gen. Greene began musing on the Marine Corps of the future. In the late 1970s, he suggested, a battalion of 1,200 Marines might be loaded aboard huge rockets and fired off to trouble spots in faraway lands. Using a huge Saturn-type rocket, he thought, it might be possible to send an expedition from the Marine base at Camp Lejeune, North Carolina, to Africa in a matter of minutes.

The intrigued reporters began asking questions. How would the Marines be placed in the rocket? Would they be strapped down in couches, sit backwards or what?

At that point, Fred Korth, then the Navy Secretary, broke in.

"General," he asked with a grin, "don't you think that for such a short trip the men could stand up?"

This episode, which conjures up a vision of burly Marines rocketing off to war at 16,000 miles an hour like straphangers on the subway, illustrates the range of military thinking about the future. It runs from the absurd to the mind-staggering.

Military planners have a particularly difficult assignment. Planners in other fields work on the assumption that the world isn't going to blow up. But military thinkers can't rule out the possibility of a nuclear holocaust.

They can't assume the present nuclear standoff won't come unstuck. Nor can they assume that the United States-backed effort to discourage the spread of nuclear weapons will succeed. Although only the United States, Britain, Russia, Communist China and France now have nuclear capability, estimates of the Atomic Energy Commission indicate that 11 other nations already have the potential to become nuclear powers if they choose to make the effort. The more nuclear powers, the greater the possibility of nuclear war.

But while planning for the possibility of Armageddon, the military can't neglect preparations for future "low-intensity" conflicts, which is Pentagon jargon for wars like Vietnam. Many authorities think the turmoil in underdeveloped lands around the globe could result in a succession of such struggles.

So it is difficult for the military to decide where to concentrate effort. "It's a pretty tough thing to sit here and postulate the kind of force we ought to have without knowing what kind of world we're going to have," says one Pentagon general, who nevertheless does that. Says another: "The scientific people say, 'Tell us what you want and give us the money and we'll build it.' So you have to decide where you want to put the money and you do that based on where you think the world is going."

A complicating factor is the lag between an idea and the time when that idea becomes an operational weapon; it can be 20 years if a technological breakthrough is required. Thus, a weapon may be outmoded by the time it enters the arsenal. Or an unexpected breakthrough—either by the United States or another power—can change the course of weapons development completely.

Such uncertainties force United States military planners to look at an incredibly broad range of possible developments. The Defense Department's research and development spending of $7 billion a year covers thousands of projects, from rockets and laser rifles to rotproof socks and diarrhea preventives.

Much of this R&D activity is secret. In the highly sensitive fields of chemical and bacteriological warfare, for example, information is almost impossible to come by, except for occasional hints of work on aerosol mists that spread dread diseases and on "incapacitants" that produce temporary paralysis or hallucinations.

Military hardware has a long life once it gets in the armed forces' inventory. True, little of it lasts as long as the C47 transport aircraft—to civilians the old DC3—which was first produced in 1935 and has taken new life in Vietnam as a gunship; some Air Force people swear it will be flying forever. But the big B52 strategic bomber first flew in 1952 and now is scheduled to remain in service until the mid-1970s. The M-1 rifle of World War II still is used, though the lighter M-16 is replacing it in Vietnam.

Most military equipment is replaced when it wears out—not as soon as someone figures out how to make a better version. The B52s eventually will be succeeded by a better airplane only because they are wearing out and not because a better bomber couldn't have been built years earlier.

One factor delaying a new heavy bomber has been Defense Secretary Robert McNamara's doubts about its usefulness—doubts that most military planners are confident will be overcome in time. But the chief reason for the slowness to change equipment is the tremendous cost of military hardware, which will continue to rise. High costs explain why the Navy is not switching more rapidly to nuclear-propelled ships, whose almost unlimited range unquestionably makes them superior to conventional Navy vessels.

Because military equipment stays in service so long, in many areas the next 30 to 35 years will see only two

183

new "generations" of military hardware. These will be equipment that is on the drawing boards or nearing production in the mid-1960s, and equipment that will follow it. The schedule for the introduction of new tanks is fairly typical.

A replacement for the M-60 tank, the current mainstay of the United States armored force, will be ready for service in the early 1970s. The new tank, lighter, lower and faster than present tanks and armed with a Shillelagh surface-to-surface guided missile, is likely to be the Army's principal tank till 1990. Then a radically different vehicle probably will come along.

Obviously, not all types of military equipment conform to this pattern of snail's pace change. This is particularly true in space and missilery.

The first intercontinental ballistic missile—the Atlas—was deployed in this country in 1959. A year later it was joined by the Titan, a comparable weapon. The Atlas already has been replaced by the Minuteman I, and the Titan is on the way out. But even before the Minuteman I is fully deployed, it is being succeeded by the Minuteman II, and Minuteman III is scheduled for production. So is Poseidon, which will replace the Polaris missiles now carried by nuclear submarines.

Other missiles are on the horizon. The Defense Department is studying an advanced ICBM as a successor to the Minuteman. This missile would be larger than the Minuteman (which is 56 feet long and weighs 69,-

184

000 pounds at launching) so that it could carry an even greater variety of "penetration aids" to thwart Russian defenses than will be packed by Poseidon and Minuteman III. The aids might include metallic chaff that could be dropped en route to confuse enemy radar; electronic jamming equipment; and such things as radar reflective devices that would appear on enemy radar scopes as other warheads. These might cause the enemy to fire antimissile missiles at the decoys while the real warheads slipped through to their targets.

Much research is being done on the problems of the reentry of missiles and their warheads into the atmosphere. United States missile experts are trying to learn, partly by underground nuclear testing, what happens when a nuclear explosion is set off near an incoming warhead. Will the warhead explode? Will its electrical parts fuse so that the missile goes awry?

This research is spurred by knowledge that the Russians are installing at least a limited antimissile system. That Soviet effort also has led the United States to step up research on the use of multiple, maneuverable warheads in a single missile as a way to compound the difficulties of defense. Both Poseidon and Minuteman III will have several warheads, and the advanced ICBM might have a dozen or more that could be released at various points along the trajectory and projected on individual courses toward different targets on the ground.

185

Guidance systems of the new Minuteman, Poseidon and succeeding missiles are expected to show marked improvement over present equipment. The better the guidance systems, the smaller the warhead needed to assure destruction of the target. Advanced Titan missiles, still deployed, have 10-megaton warheads (one megaton equals the explosive force of one million tons of TNT). Minuteman I has less than one megaton.

The anticipated guidance improvement is even prompting consideration of non-nuclear warheads for ICBMs, despite arguments that the long-range missiles are too costly to be used to deliver anything but nuclear weapons.

The drive for better missiles is accompanied by a search for ways to disperse them more widely and thereby make them less vulnerable. Safeguarding missiles from attack is a vital element of United States strategy. Washington has made it clear that it will never initiate a nuclear war. But it hopes to discourage other nations from launching a nuclear strike against the United States by protecting American missiles so well that the United States would be able to retaliate even after an attack that devastated the country and killed tens of millions of people.

At present United States missiles are dispersed in concrete silos embedded in the ground, mainly in the Great Plains, and aboard submarines. Now the Air Force again is studying the possibility of putting its advanced ICBM on railroad flatcars or trucks—a concept once rejected—and even on barges that would move around on canals. The reasoning is that if missiles could be moved about easily, they would be difficult for an enemy to find and destroy. Another idea is to sink missiles in capsules under the sea with a remote control firing mechanism; they would be anchored to the ocean floor but capable of being moved.

Even more fanciful—and in eclipse for the moment, at least—is the idea of putting a missile site on the moon. It isn't discussed publicly because this country, along with Russia and 60 others, has signed a treaty limiting military activities in outer space. The treaty, not yet ratified by the United States, prohibits the placing of weapons of mass destruction in orbit, on the moon or on other planets. It also bars all military installations from the moon and other planets. It doesn't prohibit the orbiting of military spacecraft without large weapons or the use of unmanned satellites for military purposes such as reconnaissance.

Despite the treaty, some United States military men, with an innate suspicion that the Russians eventually will cheat, argue that a lunar missile launching facility should be considered by this country as a logical sequel to the United States efforts to plant men on the moon. They would like to have plans ready to put into operation if the Russians do cheat.

Skeptics suggest that the advocates of a moon missile

187

base overlook the complications that might arise if the Russians decided to do the same thing. And many scientists scoff at the notion of lugging a nuclear warhead, plus men and equipment, 240,000 miles—only to fire it back 240,000 miles at a target that was only 5,000 miles away in the first place.

But those who favor pursuing the concept of a lunar missile site insist that if such a facility could be established by the United States, it would offer valuable advantages. They say it couldn't be put out of action by a surprise attack because of the time it would take for any enemy missile to travel from the Earth to the moon. With radio warning, United States moon missiles could blast off long before their launching site could be hit. Thus, the argument runs, the moon missile base would give the United States a secure retaliatory capacity that would add another deterrent to an atomic attack.

Not quite so farfetched-sounding is the speculation on possible military applications for the $1.5 billion Manned Orbiting Laboratory (MOL), which may be launched as early as 1969.

The MOL does not face any overpowering technological obstacles. It will consist of a proven Gemini capsule, plus the laboratory itself, which will be attached just below the Gemini at blastoff. An advanced Titan booster will launch the MOL. The astronauts will ride in the Gemini on the trip into orbit. Once there, they will move into the roomier laboratory, which will

188

measure 41 feet by 10 feet, to do a variety of chores. When their mission is over, they will move back into the Gemini, cut loose the MOL, which will stay in orbit for future reuse, and ride the Gemini back home.

Some military planners think the MOL could be turned into a major military weapon relatively easily if there were a breach in the outer space treaty. Rendezvousing several MOLs, for instance, and docking them into one connected unit, would provide room for both crew and equipment to carry out a variety of military chores. The connected MOLs could serve as a command post for ground, sea, air and maybe space forces, or as a launching platform for missiles. (Only the latter is banned by the treaty.)

Because the Russians can be expected to improve their ability to deliver nuclear warheads and because they have begun to deploy an antimissile system, work on a United States antimissile system is going ahead. Production of the well-publicized Nike-X system could begin as soon as a go-ahead is given.

The Nike-X system uses long-range Spartan missiles to intercept enemy missiles 300 to 400 miles from targets. The Spartans are backed up by extremely fast Sprint missiles to catch enemy warheads that slip past the Spartans. The system would use highly sophisticated radar units, either already designed or under development, that would constantly scan the skies for incoming missiles. The radars would be linked to computers that would be able to sort out the decoys by "reading" the radar pulses and to direct defensive missiles to the enemy's warheads.

The cost of such a system has been estimated at from $4 billion to $40 billion. The low estimate is for a "thin" defense against a limited capability by the Red Chinese to launch missiles against the United States. The top figure is for a much more elaborate defense against a Soviet threat. The Chinese are expected to achieve limited nuclear-missile capability by the mid-1970s, and this prospect is making it increasingly likely that the United States will decide to build some form of antimissile system.

The laser, a device that emits a beam of "pure" light, also figures in thinking about missile defenses. Experimental laser devices are being installed at Cape Kennedy to track missiles by measuring the time it takes to bounce light pulses off them, then converting the time into distance.

The laser's ability to track a missile almost automatically leads to speculation on its use in an antimissile system. Besides following an attacking missile, the laser beam conceivably could cause its destruction by burning key components. Since a laser beam travels at the speed of light—186,000 miles a second—even a 16,000-mile-an-hour missile would be a slow-moving target.

Some basic problems remain to be solved before the

laser is even theoretically workable as an antimissile weapon. But the laser is only six years old, and huge sums of money are being spent on research aimed at overcoming the obstacles. Meanwhile, a host of other military uses for the laser are taking shape.

A laser range-finder for artillery spotters is being purchased for testing by the Army. It works on the same principle as the missile-tracking laser. Moreover, the laser may prove to be the "death-ray" gun long popular in science fiction.

The power of a laser is measured in joules, a unit equal to one watt of energy in one second. A 500-joule laser has killed a rat; 1,500-joule lasers are in operation and experts say that when power and heat problems are solved—the experts are confident they will be—billion-watt lasers will be built.

Only one-fourth of a joule will cause permanent eye damage; not long ago a researcher a mile from the source caught a laser beam in an eye and suffered a severely burned retina. A laser rifle could blind an enemy in combat and might well kill him. It could also touch off explosives or set fire to wood.

Satellites also may play a role in the defense against missiles. The Defense Department is talking guardedly about a new all-purpose satellite that would combine the jobs done now by Samos, the photo-intelligence reconnaissance satellite; Tiros, which gathers weather data; Vela, the satellite designed to detect nuclear explosions in space; and Midas, which would serve as an early-warning alarm of a missile firing by detecting ballistic missile exhaust plumes from their infrared radiation.

The experts see this possibility: An orbiting satellite spots a missile taking off from the USSR. It charts the missile's direction and sees that it is heading for the United States. The satellite flashes a command to an American antimissile missile, which takes off and meets the Russian missile far from United States shores, destroying it—a victim of war between machines.

As there are now antimissile missiles, so there may be antisatellite satellites. Under consideration is a satellite, either manned or unmanned, that would be fired aloft when, as an Air Force man delicately puts it, "noncooperative satellites were spotted." The antisatellite weapon would inspect the stranger and blast it out of the skies if it proved unfriendly.

Much of the planning for the distant future focuses on ways to guard against or survive a cataclysmic nuclear war. But some military men suggest that eventually nuclear weapons may not be associated exclusively with mass, widespread destruction.

What they foresee is further development of relatively small tactical nuclear weapons. The Army already has equipped some large ground force units with atomic howitzers and with Davy Crockett nuclear rockets, which can be fired from launchers not much larger than World War II bazookas.

Now ordnance specialists seek still smaller nuclear weapons that could be used right down to the squad level and that would produce less radioactive debris than present nuclear equipment. One scientist goes so far as to say he can foresee "the time when for all practical purposes you won't be able to tell the difference between a small tactical nuclear explosion and a big chemical blast. It'll really be just more bang for a buck."

At the same time, the experts also contemplate the use of non-nuclear missiles. The missiles and space division of Lockheed Aircraft Corporation, builder of the Polaris, has proposed using the missiles with non-nuclear warheads against some targets in Vietnam. A Navy man suggests such weapons could have been used effectively against the oil storage tanks in Hanoi and Haiphong. An admiral foresees missiles with interchangeable warheads and interchangeable missions—missiles with nuclear warheads for strategic use, the same missiles with non-nuclear warheads for tactical use.

Such schemes are all part of a drive for highly flexible military forces. Another key aspect in this flexibility is a far higher degree of mobility than United States forces now have.

The giant C5A aircraft, under development by Lockheed, should enhance military mobility as much as any single item of military hardware now in the works. At 700,000 pounds, the C5A will be twice as big as any other transport in the United States military aircraft fleet.

In 13 hours 42 C5As could have handled the 15,000 troops and their equipment moved to Europe in 1963 in Exercise Big Lift—which actually took 63 hours and 243 aircraft. With its capacity to fly large troop loads anywhere at high speeds, the C5A obviously will diminish the need to station United States soldiers abroad. Beyond the C5A, 200 of which probably will be in operation by the early 1970s, may be even bigger transports.

Another avenue of military aircraft research and development points toward planes that would travel at hypersonic speeds—4,000 miles an hour or more. The military is looking at two types of these craft, both of which would be much smaller than the C5A.

One would be a 5,300-mile-an-hour plane that could be turned out in passenger, reconnaissance and bomber versions. The other would be a 15,000-mile-an-hour craft that would soar through space like a rocket but would be able to take off and land like an airplane. Some researchers say this craft could replace huge rocket boosters such as Saturn for some space missions, providing great savings because of its ability to return to Earth and fly again.

Even though the plane would match a rocket's speed, its gradual acceleration and deceleration would mean that crew and passengers would not suffer the stresses that rocket travelers must endure. These stresses are one of the considerations that cause most military men to rule out rockets for transporting personnel, the speculations of Marine Corps Commandant Greene to the contrary.

Planners also expect United States military forces to increase their capability to move men and equipment over and under the seas. They envision huge submarines that could operate in relative safety at levels far deeper than the 1,000 feet or so that United States subs now reach. The subs would approach hostile shores, then transfer troops and gear to tractor-like vehicles that would crawl along the bottom until they emerged on the beach.

Sea speeds will rise sharply. This will result from application of the air-cushion principle to ships. Air-cushion vessels can glide over water on a pancake of compressed air provided by internal blower systems. Because they are almost completely free from water resistance, high speeds are possible.

The Navy foresees a 100-knot aircraft carrier by the turn of the century (present carriers have top speeds of 35 knots). Big landing craft and cargo vessels that would be equally fast also are possible. Small air-cushion vehicles already have been introduced for civilian use, particularly in England, and the Navy has tested three air-cushion boats in the Mekong Delta region of South Vietnam.

Land mobility, already given a tremendous boost by the extensive use of the helicopter in Vietnam, also will

195

increase. Under development is a jet flying belt for the individual soldier. It would enable him to move at 60 miles an hour and leapfrog enemy defenses.

Air-cushion vehicles, which can travel over land as well as water, might further increase the Army's mobility. Though some researchers are skeptical about their use on civilian highways because of imprecise steering and other problems, they appear well suited for speeding over open countryside and rivers with large loads of troops and supplies.

— FREDERICK TAYLOR